THE COMPLETE BOOK OF
Fruit

An illustrated guide to over 400 species and varieties of fruit from all over the world

THE COMPLETE BOOK OF
Fruit

An illustrated guide to over 400 species and varieties of fruit from all over the world

Dick Pijpers · Jac. G. Constant · Kees Jansen

GALLERY BOOKS
An Imprint of W. H. Smith Publishers Inc.
112 Madison Avenue
New York City 10016

Adapted from the Dutch by Multimedia Publications
(UK) Ltd

Translation: AGET Language Services, London
Design: Ron Putto, Matthew Ward
Production: Karen Bromley

First published in the Netherlands by Uitgeverij
Het Spectrum BV, Parkvoorn 4, 3454 JR De Meern

First published in the United States of America 1986
by Gallery Books, an imprint of W.H. Smith
Publishers Inc., 112 Madison Avenue, New York,
NY 10016

Typeset by Keene Graphics Ltd, London, UK
Printed by Cayfosa, Barcelona, Spain
Dep. Leg. B-10624-1986
ISBN 0 8317 3672-0

Contents

Introduction

This book is all about fruit, in particular the wide range of exotic fruits that are now becoming available in North America and Europe. So, what *is* a fruit? Opinions are divided — botanists say one thing, cooks another. In the botanical sense a fruit is simply the seed-carrying part of a plant; in this sense tomatoes, aubergines, cucumbers and peppers are all fruits, although they are generally used as vegetables. That is why you will not find them in this book. The authors have adopted the everyday distinction between 'fruit' and 'vegetables', a distinction based on culinary use rather than botanical fact. So apples, generally used for dessert dishes, have a place in this book, but tomatoes, generally used for savoury dishes, do not.

Another controversial area is taste. Can one define what a fruit is in terms of taste? Attempts have been made to develop scientifically valid taste categories and generally accepted ways of describing them, but without much success. We simply have to accept that all taste descriptions — sweet, sour, bitter, tart, acid, spicy, aromatic, etc. — are subjective. Even so, most fruit tastes cluster into the sweet or sweetish category, hence the general preference for using them in desserts rather than savouries.

Three points to remember as you browse through this book: all the fruits are organized according to the Latin name of the family to which they belong, the reason being that some families simply do not have English names; the measurements given in the captions are the measurements of the individual fruits photographed, not necessarily the average measurements of the variety or species concerned; the heading 'Producer Countries' refers to those countries from which America and Europe mainly import their fruit.

A fruit orchard in full bloom in Afghanistan. Many fruit varieties originally came from Asia.

The world of fruit

In recent years the range of fruit available in the West has has changed dramatically. There has been a great influx of exotic fruits, very few of which our parents or grandparents have ever heard of, unless they are exceptionally well-travelled. At the same time many familiar and traditional species have suddenly disappeared and been replaced by new ones. Every year, it seems, we are introduced to new hybrid fruits with curious-sounding names. Not being able to appreciate the reasons for all these changes, we tend to feel a bit confused. Even fruit dealers themselves are occasionally overwhelmed by the number of fruit varieties on offer.

'Disappearing' fruit

One of the most striking changes in the fruit world has been the disappearance of traditional favourites. Up until a few years after World War II every housewife knew apple species such as Ribston and Miller's Seedling. Today these varieties are almost unobtainable. They have been replaced by new ones and we are left wistfully recalling the delicious fruits of yesteryear.

What lies behind this modern trend? It is closely linked with wide social changes, of course. Populations in Europe and North America have increased and become concentrated in urban areas. As a result, the demand for fruit has increased. The seasonal bounties of the orchard have to be transported greater distances and so the need for long-term storage has arisen. Greater consumer purchasing power has also fueled a new demand for fruit out of season — we now want strawberries at Christmas, avocado pears all year round.

Many traditional species are simply not suitable for longer storage. Beauty of Bath, for example, is a splendid eating apple — as long as it is eaten ripe direct from the tree — but it is very easily bruised and travels badly. It is at its best immediately after picking, and goes off rapidly after a day or two. Result: housewives today seldom see Beauty of Bath in the greengrocer's or the supermarket.

'Old' species of fruit have become less suitable for new markets for a variety of other reasons. A fruit grower may opt for a new species because the old one is too prone to disease, or because it is too expensive to harvest, or because it crops so heavily over a short period that the price slumps, or because it produces too small a yield to be profitable.

New species

Shortly after World War II, in response to these new market requirements, scientists began to work intensively on improving the quality of fruit by crossbreeding, which up until then had been the province of enterprising amateurs. Crossbreeding was in fact nothing new. The Greeks, the Romans and other civilizations had all experimented with it. Now, for the first time, research was supported by the full resources of modern science and was in direct response to urgent market needs. Crossbreeding trials began in the United States and in Europe. The aim was to produce better varieties — attractive, tasty products that not only keep well but also crop heavily, are highly resistant to disease and easy to harvest.
Crossbreeding involves transferring pollen from the flower of one species or variety to the stigma, the female reproductive organ, of a closely related species or variety. For example, a variety that keeps well but is rather tasteless will be crossed with a tastier variety that may not keep so well. The aim is to combine the best of both. However, the process is very long and complicated. Cultivated as well as wild varieties may be used in crossbreeding and a wide spectrum of characteristics are juggled with.

The seeds produced by a crossbred plant must be allowed to develop into a fully grown bush or tree. Only when it has borne fruit can the crop scientist assess whether his attempts have been successful and whether the hybrid is worth further development. If it is, the new variety is further tested by selected farmers and growers. If it continues to come up to expectations, it will then be made available to commercial growers. So, it will take years before the consumer gets to know about a new variety.

Even a variety with outstanding characteristics can be unsuccessful on the market. Take Jonagold, for example. This apple was produced in 1943 in the United States from a cross between the Golden Delicious and the Jonathan. It was not successful, possibly because of its acidity and its red-on-yellow colouring. But when it was introduced into Europe in the sixties, fruit growers and consumers raved about it! Reliable early cropping appealed to the fruit growers and the colour and taste appealed to the consumer. The Jonagold rapidly invaded the fruit stalls of Western Europe.

Gene banks

The search for new fruit varieties continues all over the world. Naturally, fruits that have the greatest commercial potential dominate research efforts. Apples, pears, plums, peaches, berry fruits, citrus fruits, pineapples, mangoes

A fruit and vegetable shop in Israel

and a few other tropical and subtropical fruits are the most popular and so receive the most attention.

The number of new varieties created by crossbreeding programmes can be enormous. At the experimental fruit farm in Wilhelminadorp in the Netherlands, for example, new species of fruit from all over the world are tested to see whether they can withstand a temperate climate. In 1984 there were 162 new varieties of apple being tested there. Consumers will never see most of them because they will not become commercial varieties. But not all the 'unsuccessfuls' are lost. Nor have the 'forgotten' species of yesteryear been lost. Their genes are stored by the International Board of Plant Genetic Resources, a body set up in collaboration with other organizations such as the Food and Agriculture Organization of the United

When the Spanish orange season comes to an end, cargoes of oranges from elsewhere start to arrive in the ports of Western Europe. From January to March they come mainly from Israel and Morocco; after that, they come from South Africa, South America and the southern United States, the peak month being August. Since bulk shipments can now be kept for quite long periods of time in gigantic cold storage facilities, the availability of oranges in the shops can easily be extended to October, when Spanish oranges are available again. Today oranges and most other citrus fruits are available throughout the year.

The banana has a similar history. One advantage of this tropical fruit is that it can be harvested unripe and will ripen during transport and storage. During shipment, and more especially afterwards, bananas are stored in very

Above: *measuring growth rate (left), and an experimental research station (right).* Top right: *peach harvesting in Italy.* Middle and bottom right: *grading oranges in Spain, and oranges crated up for shipment on an Israeli kibbutz.*

Nations (FAO). Many specially selected varieties are kept in store, even though they are of no commercial interest at present, to be used as raw material for future research.

These gene banks contain an enormous wealth of plant material not only for fruit species but for other food and cash crops as well. One research station in England grows over 2,000 varieties of apple. There is also a gene bank in Belgium which has 630 varieties of pear; there is another big gene bank for pears at Angers in France.

Ultimately all of these gene banks will computerize all the genetic information they contain so that plant breeders can quickly locate the precise characteristics they happen to be looking for and the species and varieties in which they occur.

Transport and storage
Modern and rapid means of transport and greatly improved refrigeration techniques have also had a big impact on the world fruit market. Tropical fruits can now be supplied on a regular basis and almost every kind of fruit can be stored and distributed in such a way that it can be bought all year round.

A good example is the orange. In the past, only Spanish oranges were available in Western and Central Europe. Because they are harvested between October and December, they could only be bought during these months. Now, thanks to modern transport and new refrigeration techniques, the situation is very different.

special conditions. The post-harvesting ripening process takes place almost exclusively in fully automated ripening warehouses where the bananas are stored after shipment. By careful monitoring of temperature, air humidity and ventilation, the ripening process is controlled so that the bananas are at exactly the right stage of ripeness when they go on sale in the shops. The distribution of many other kinds of fruit can now be spread virtually throughout the year using similar storage methods. For example, when the European plum harvest comes to an end, plums from countries like South Africa begin to arrive in the shops.

Similar 'supply relays' between the temperate and tropical areas of the northern and southern hemispheres operate for many other fruits — grapes, peaches, apricots, for example. Even soft fruit, which perishes very quickly, can now be flown in from all over the world and quantities are limited only by the price the consumer is prepared to pay.

Another way to ensure a supply of out-of-season fruit is to extend the cropping season artificially. This is done with strawberries, for example. By retarding the development of young strawberry plants by putting them in cold store and planting them out only at a very late stage, flower and fruit formation can be delayed until after the normal season ends.

Exotic fruit
An ever increasing diversity of exotic fruits has crept onto the North American and European market in recent years. The first of these exotic pioneers found their way into Indian, Asian and African shops used chiefly by immigrant communities. Supply of such delicacies is often limited and irregular, and because demand is small andbecause such fruits are not yet available out of season, most major fruit importers show little interest in them.

But this situation changes rapidly when non-immigrant communities 'discover' what they are missing! At that point, major importers *do* become interested, planting

programmes expand in the producer countries, and growers in other countries with suitable climates begin experimenting with new types to corner the market. Consumer interest grows as prices drop and the fruit becomes more widely available. The whole process of supply and demand is stimulated and within a relatively short time the fruit becomes a familiar sight in the shops. This has been the story of the the mango and the kiwi fruit, though much of the success of the latter has been due to intensive promotion on the part of the New Zealand Kiwi Fruit Authority.

At present there are a number of exotic fruits poised to break into Western markets. Fruits such as the lychee, the pawpaw and the guava are beginning to invade the more ambitious supermarket chains. Others such as the salak are approaching this phase. Many others, as yet relatively unknown, can be expected to generate interest in the coming years. This is especially true of hybrids from closely related varieties, often discovered accidentally during research work. A well known example is the ugli, an unattractive but delicious fruit of obscure origins, which in its present-day form is a cross between a tangerine, a grapefruit and a Seville orange.

Such hybrids are constantly being developed, especially among the citrus fruits, and many of them are tried out on the American and European consumers. Examples are the Israeli pomelo (a cross between a shaddock and a grapefruit), tangelo varieties such as the minneola (a tangerine crossed with a grapefruit) and hybrids of the kumquat, whose names — citrangequat, orangequat and limequat - indicate their parentage.

9

Actinidiae
Kiwi fruit

The family of climbing plants called *Actinidiae* is native to East Asia and the Himalayas. It comprises 40 species with neatly formed leaves and white to brownish flowers. All the species are dioecious — in other words, the male and the female flowers develop at the same time but on separate plants. For pollination to take place, there must be male plants near female plants, so that insects can carry the pollen of the males to the stigmas of the females. The fuzzy fruits contain up to 800 seeds, generally arranged radially. Of the 40 species only three produce edible fruits. *Actinidia arguto* (Japanese name: *kokowa)* is grown mainly in Japan and the Soviet Union, and *A. kolomikta* chiefly in the Soviet Union. Neither are found on the market elsewhere because they are difficult to transport. The opposite is true of *A. chinensis,* which is also called the Chinese gooseberry.

The kiwi fruit came originally from southern China, where the plant and fruit are called *yang tao.* At the beginning of this century the plant was taken by a missionary to New Zealand where it thrived. The fruit was renamed after New Zealand's national symbol, the kiwi bird.

For many years the kiwi fruit was only grown and eaten in New Zealand. Around 1940, however, by which time several commercially attractive varieties had been developed, production began elsewhere. From 1960 onwards, the fruit started to become enormously popular all over the world. Because the kiwi vine is adaptable and grows in most situations provided there are no night frosts, it is now grown on a commercial basis in many countries. For taste and size, however, New Zealand kiwi fruit are still the best. Thanks to staggered harvesting and good keeping qualities — between four and six months at a temperature of 32°F (0°C) — kiwi fruit are now on sale almost all the year round.

Kiwi fruit are ripe when they are slightly soft to the touch. The juice contains an enzyme that breaks down protein. Marinading meat in the juice or rubbing the fruit over meat tenderizes it, so that it cooks more quickly. The same effect can be achieved by cooking the meat with the fruit for a short time.

△ Hayward, 2¼in (59mm) long

Kiwi Fruit or **Chinese Gooseberry**
(Actinidia chinensis)

DESCRIPTION: Round or elongated, brown and fuzzy, approximately 2½in (7cm) long, and weighing 1-4oz (25-100g). The green flesh has a white core and the black, edible seeds are arranged radially. The sweet-sour taste is delicate and refreshing, reminiscent of a combination of gooseberry, melon and strawberry.

COUNTRY OF ORIGIN: Southern China.

PRODUCER COUNTRIES: New Zealand, Australia, Israel, France, Italy, Spain, Guernsey, Chile, California.

AVAILABILITY: All year from various producer countries.

USE: Peel or cut in half and scoop out flesh; can be eaten on its own or sliced into fruit salads, cakes, cocktails, ice-creams or used to garnish meat or fish. Bake or roast meat in the juice to tenderize it. Jam cannot be made with kiwi fruit as an enzyme it contains prevents jam setting.

KEEPING QUALITIES: Unripe fruits keep in the refrigerator for four to six weeks, and at room temperature for a few days. Ripe fruits keep in the refrigerator for a few days. Unripe fruits ripen within 24 hours if kept in a plastic bag or aluminium foil together with a ripe apple, pear or banana — the ethylene gas given off by the ripe fruit accelerates ripening.

NUTRITIONAL VALUE: Very rich in vitamin C (1 kiwi = 10 lemons); also contains vitamins A and D; 39 Kcal per 100g serving.

INDUSTRIAL PROCESSING: Canned in syrup.

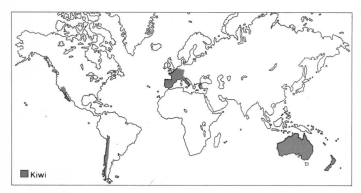

■ Kiwi

△ Bruno, 3in (71mm) long   ▽ Abbott, 3¼in (86mm)long

Varieties

Abbott An early variety, elongated in shape with fuzzy skin. Average weight 2½oz (70g). Keeps well. Taste very close to gooseberry.

Allison Very similar in shape, appearance and taste to 'Abbott', but appears later on the market.

Bruno An attractive, small, oval variety with outstanding taste, especially popular in West Germany. Average weight 2oz (55g). Keeps reasonably well.

Hayward This late-flowering variety is generally considered the best. The plump, oval fruits weigh on average 3oz (80g), though the heaviest ones can weigh up to 4½oz (120g). Much sweeter than other varieties; also keeps better.

Matua Small, attractive variety mainly grown in California.

Monty Oval fruits seldom heavier than 2oz (60g). Fuzzier and not as sweet as other varieties, with a slightly bitter aftertaste.

Planchon This cigar-shaped, very fuzzy variety comes mainly from Italy. It is gradually losing out to other varieties, because it does not keep well.

Tomuri A new variety, like 'Matua' grown mainly in California. Excellent flavour. Similar to 'Hayward' in weight and appearance but very light brown in colour.

Anacardiaceae
Mango, bauno, gandaria, ambarella, hogplum, Jamaica plum

All the 600 or so members of the *Anacardiaceae* family are trees or bushes. They grow in tropical and temperate zones, but are absent from Central and Western Europe. However, some members of the family, such as the wig tree and the velvet tree (an ornamental species) grow around the Mediterranean. Some members of the family produce edible fruits or seeds — cashew and pistachio nuts, for example. Other fruits of the *Anacardiaceae* are the ambarella, the gandaria and the bauno from Southeast Asia, and the Jamaica plum from tropical South America. The best known representative of the family is the mango, or mangga, eaten all over the world and grown in many tropical and subtropical countries.

The mango is to the tropics what the apple is to temperate climes. There are thousands of varieties ranging in size from plums (small) to melons (large). Export varieties tend to be medium-sized.

If they are not grafted to dwarf rootstocks, mango trees will eventually grow to a height of 30-100ft (10-30m). They bloom abundantly, with long tresses of greenish-yellow flowers; these are often used for religious ceremonies, especially in India. Probably the plant originally came from India and/or Malaysia. In the 16th century, it was introduced by the Portuguese into South Africa and Brazil. Mangoes go off quickly, so overseas exports only became possible with the advent of air freight and refrigerator ships. Mangoes are now cultivated on a large scale mainly in Southeast Asia, Central and South Africa, Israel, Brazil, Central America, Mexico and Florida.

Ripe mangoes can vary in colour from green, through yellow, orange and rosy red, to purple. Quality can vary considerably and is determined by, among other things, the amount of fibre in the orange-yellow flesh and the pungency of the turpentine taste in the skin. Chilling makes this taste less noticeable; served ice-cold, the taste disappears altogether. Careful transport and storage is extremely important. Mangoes for export are harvested unripe. If the temperature during shipment is above 50°F (10°C), the fruit will continue to ripen in transit and the taste will be poor. On the other hand, fruits that have been kept too cold often develop grey spots on the skin; like mangoes harvested too early, they are best used for making mango chutney.

Properly handled fruits kept at room temperature continue to ripen well after harvesting. Mangoes are ripe when they give off a strong smell, are soft to the touch, and have the odd brown or black spot on their skins. In this condition they will keep for two days in the salad drawer of the refrigerator. The taste of a properly ripened mango is sweet, spicy, rather oily and faintly resembles the taste of peach. The tough skin is inedible. At the centre of the edible flesh is a large flat seed that can only be removed easily in very ripe fruits.

Mangoes are very rich in vitamin A; one mango contains twenty times as much vitamin A as an orange of equal size. Some people suffer stomach complaints after drinking milk or alcohol shortly after eating mango.

Mangoes for export are harvested unripe

■ Mango

Mango or **Mangga**
DESCRIPTION: Kidney-shaped fruit, 2½-12in (6-30cm) long, with a stiff, leathery and inedible skin. The colour of the ripe fruit varies — green, yellow, orange, rosy pink, even purple - and the skin may have a few spots. In the centre of the orange-yellow flesh, which can be fibrous in texture depending on variety and ripeness, is a large flat stone which is often difficult to remove. The flesh is sweet and spicy, with a slightly turpentine taste.
COUNTRIES OF ORIGIN: India, Malaysia.
PRODUCER COUNTRIES: India, Pakistan, Egypt, Israel, Sudan, Mali, Kenya, Upper Volta, South Africa, Brazil, Venezuela, Surinam, Mexico, California, Philippines.
AVAILABILITY: Throughout the year from different producer countries.
USE: Cut around the fruit lengthways, scoop out both halves and extract the stone. Ripe fruits can also be peeled and the flesh cut off in slices lengthways. The flesh can be eaten fresh, sprinkled with lemon or orange juice, or used chopped in desserts (with cream, whipped cream, yoghurt, custard, etc.), fruit salads, hors d'oeuvres (with ham, for example, or sprinkled with curry powder and ground cloves) or in meat dishes.
KEEPING QUALITIES: Ripe fruits keep one or two days in refrigerator; unripe fruits one week at room temperature, or up to two weeks in refrigerator salad drawer.
NUTRITIONAL VALUE: Very rich in vitamin A, traces of vitamins B and C, a few minerals.
INDUSTRIAL PROCESSING: Chutneys, juice.

Varieties

Alphonso A variety derived from 'Mulgoba', characteristically kidney-shaped and sharply spicy in taste. The colour depends on the producing region and varies from green with a red bloom to yellow with red spots. Cultivated in widely differing areas. Western European

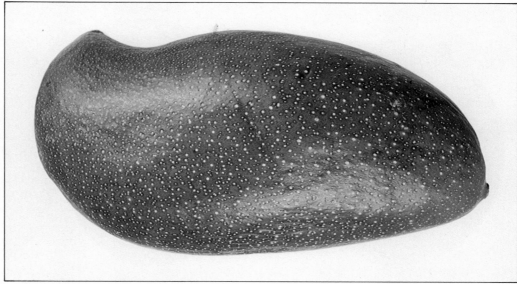

△ Arumanis, 7in (18cm) long   ▽ Haden, 4in (11cm) long

imports generally come from South Africa, Southeast Asia, and Florida.

Arumanis A most delicious mango from Indonesia, chiefly cultivated on the island of Java. The fruit is green in colour and has a mild taste. Supplies are irregular but when found are well worth buying.

Benett This variety, derived from 'Alphonso', comes from Florida and is mainly grown in Kenya and Tanzania for the European market and in Sudan for the Middle Eastern market. The flesh is delicious and the stone is easy to remove.

Golden Jubilee A beautiful, spherical mango, golden-yellow in colour, with a deep reddish bloom when ripe. Grown exclusively in Florida. The flesh is soft — like that of a peach — and does not have the spicy taste characteristic of most other mangoes.

Haden or **Heyden** This variety, derived from 'Mulgoba', is a favourite with fruit growers everywhere, but is mainly grown in South Africa and Hawaii. The oval-shaped fruits, green and red in colour, can grow very large, weighing up to 1lb 2oz (500g). The taste is sweet and mild.

△ Mulgoba, 3½in (93mm) diameter

Irwin A good quality variety developed in Florida, although European imports come mainly from Kenya and Tanzania. The fruits are 4-6in (10-15cm) long, light orange-yellow in colour with a red bloom. The flesh is mildly spicy and the stone relatively small.

Julie A variety grown mainly in the Caribbean but also in Kenya and South Africa. The taste is good but not exceptional. The variety adapts well to widely differing climates.

Kent or **Keith** A mango variety developed from 'Mulgoba', about 6in (15cm) long and 10½oz (300g) in weight, and with a small stone. Cultivated in Florida as a late species, 'Kent' is harvested in July/August for the European market.

△ Kent, 4in (109mm) diameter   ▽ Zill, 4in (109mm) diameter

△ Tommy Atkins, 5in (127mm) diameter

Langra This variety is similar to 'Alphonso', but difference in appearance is due to varying soils and climates. 'Langras' imported into Europe come mainly from Sudan. They have few fibres and taste excellent.

Mulgoba A very important mango variety cultivated in large quantities in numerous production areas; a parent of many new varieties. Europe imports 'Mulgobas' from all producing regions. The very soft, sweet flesh tastes 'peachier' than that of any other mango variety.

Ngowo Grown almost exclusively in Central Africa, the fruits are flattish-round and vary in colour from green

(unripe) to pale orange. A good eating variety with a slightly spicy taste.

Pairi or **Pathiri** An important mango variety in Sudan, where the fruit is called 'father of the fish', probably because of its elongated shape. The fruits are approximately 8in (20cm) long, light green in colour, ripening to yellow. 'Pairis' on the European market come mainly from Thailand.

Tommy Atkins Cultivated mainly in Florida, delicate and spicy in taste and smell, and orange-yellow in colour with a bright red blush. Its very juicy flesh has few fibres. Only sporadically obtainable in Europe.

Zill An outstanding mango variety but difficult to recognize as its shape and colour are strongly affected by conditions in the growing area. 'Zills' from South Africa, for example, are heart-shaped and have a green-red colour; those from Kenya are kidney-shaped and yellow. In all cases, the taste is excellent.

KEEPING QUALITIES: As mango (see page 13).
NUTRITIONAL VALUE: Not known.
INDUSTRIAL PROCESSING: Jams and chutneys.

△ Ambarella, 3in (76mm) diameter ▽ Hogplum, 2in (49mm) diameter

USE: Peel should be removed and the flesh of the sweet varieties eaten fresh or used as mango. Sour varieties are mainly used for making chutneys and preserves.
KEEPING QUALITIES: As mango (see page 13).
NUTRITIONAL VALUE: Not known.
INDUSTRIAL PROCESSING: None.

Ambarella
(Spondias cytherea)
DESCRIPTION: The fruit, 2-4in (5-10cm) long, is round or oval and distinguished by five indentations that run over three-quarters of its length. As it ripens it changes from bright green to yellow with brown spots. The skin is soft and thin and the stone leathery. The white or yellowish flesh is soft and fibrous, smells strongly of turpentine and tastes sweet and resinous.
COUNTRY OF ORIGIN: Tahiti.
PRODUCER COUNTRIES: Thailand, Indonesia, Malaysia, Philippines.
AVAILABILITY: May to October.
USE: Peel the fruit or cut through and scoop out. Eat ripe fruits fresh or treat as mango. Can also be made into juice or processed into jam or chutney. Cooked flesh tastes a bit like pineapple.

Bauno
(Mangifera verticillata)
DESCRIPTION: A close relative of the mango, somewhat resembling a small mango. The orange-yellow flesh is very fibrous, soft and aromatic. It has a pleasant, slightly sour taste, reminiscent of apricot.
COUNTRY OF ORIGIN: Philippines.
PRODUCER COUNTRY: Philippines.
AVAILABILITY: August and September.
USE: As mango (see page 13).
KEEPING QUALITIES: As mango.
NUTRITIONAL VALUE: Not known.
INDUSTRIAL PROCESSING: None.

Gandaria
(Bouea macrophylla)
DESCRIPTION: The plum-sized fruits, 1½-2½in (4-6cm) long, very much resemble small mangoes. The skin is soft and thin and turns from green to yellow as the fruit ripens. When ripe the fruit is soft to the touch. The yellow or orange flesh is soft and a little sticky, and tastes sweet or tart depending on the variety. The stone is even more difficult to remove than that of the mango.
COUNTRIES OF ORIGIN: Malaysia, Indonesia.
PRODUCER COUNTRIES: Malaysia, Thailand, Indonesia.
AVAILABILITY: February to May.

△ Gandaria, 1¼in / 31mm) diameter

Hogplum
(Spondias mombin)
DESCRIPTION: An oval, yellow fruit with a large, hard stone, and 1-2in (2-5cm) long. The fruit has a distinct turpentine odour. The soft flesh tastes sharply acid and somewhat aromatic.
COUNTRY OF ORIGIN: Tropical America.
PRODUCER COUNTRIES: Central America, Central Africa.
AVAILABILITY: June to December.
USE: Eat fresh, including peel, or process into fruit compote.

KEEPING QUALITIES: A few days at room temperature.
NUTRITIONAL VALUE: Not known.
INDUSTRIAL PROCESSING: None.

Jamaica Plum
(Spondias purpurea)
DESCRIPTION: Red or yellowish-brown fruit, otherwise like the hogplum, but with a better, sweeter and less sharp taste.
COUNTRY OF ORIGIN: Tropical America.
PRODUCER COUNTRIES: Central America, Philippines.
AVAILABILITY: June to December.
USE: As hogplum.
KEEPING QUALITIES: A few days at room temperature.
NUTRITIONAL VALUE: Not known.
INDUSTRIAL PROCESSING: None.

Annonaceae

Cherimoya, soursop, custard apple, sugar apple

Of the 20 or so genera which make up the family *Annonaceae* and together account for more than 2,000 species only a few produce edible fruits, and only some of these will ever become commercial fruits for the good reason that they do not keep at all well. A very good example is the genus *Annona*. These are medium-sized trees that originally came from Central and South America. During the 16th century some of them were introduced into other countries. Many of them produce delicious fruit but they are often only eaten in the places where they grow because they do not travel well. The problem of transport is not solved by refrigeration because few of them can tolerate temperatures below 55°F (14°C). So shipment by air offers the only solution, but this puts the price up considerably in the shops and the price will only come down when consumers start buying in larger quantities.

One of the better known *Annona* species that travels well enough to be exportable is the cherimoya, which ripens at room temperature after being harvested unripe. Two other related species, the sugar apple and the custard apple, do not travel quite so well but do appear periodically on the market — although when they do, they are often incorrectly labelled as cherimoyas. The soursop also appears very occasionally in the shops and may become more familiar in the future as juice, syrup or jelly. For fruit growers other varieties have potential, such as the atemoya, a cross between a cherimoya and a sugar apple, although only time will tell whether this particular cross will survive commercially.

All *Annona* species have one thing in common: they are composite fruits, made up of scaly sections that grow together fir-cone fashion.

Cherimoya
(Annona cherimoya)

DESCRIPTION: Round or heart-shaped composite fruits, weighing 9½-22oz (250-600g). The greenish purple skin is divided into oblong scales which overlap each other like roof tiles, but form a complete outer case. The white, creamy flesh contains inedible black pips. Flavour is sour-sweet with a scent reminiscent of strawberry and pineapple. The fruit is ripe when the skin begins to blacken.

COUNTRIES OF ORIGIN: Peru, Ecuador.

PRODUCER COUNTRIES: Spain, Portugal, Israel, Brazil, Thailand, Indonesia.

AVAILABILITY: All year round from various producer countries.

USE: Cut fruits lengthways, remove pips, and scoop out the flesh. Eat fresh or in fruit salad, or mix with milk, yoghurt, etc.

KEEPING QUALITIES: Two or three days at room temperature.

NUTRITIONAL VALUE: 114 Kcal vitamin C per 100g serving.

INDUSTRIAL PROCESSING: Not known.

Soursop
(Annona muricata)

DESCRIPTION: A cigar-shaped black fruit, up to 22oz (600g) in weight, with a bright green skin covered with warts or soft thorns. The composite fruit is ripe when soft to the touch. Each part of the fruit contains a quantity of creamy white flesh and a hard, brownish-black pip. The taste is sour-sweet and refreshing, with a very characteristic aroma.

COUNTRIES OF ORIGIN: Peru, Ecuador.

PRODUCER COUNTRIES: Indonesia, Venezuela, Puerto Rico.

AVAILABILITY: All year round but sporadic due to poor keeping quality.

USE: Scoop out the flesh and use in desserts mixed with ice-cream or yoghurt, or in cakes. Can also be used for jam and jelly, in milkshakes and sorbets.

KEEPING QUALITIES: As cherimoya.

NUTRITIONAL VALUE: Not known.

INDUSTRIAL PROCESSING: Fruit syrup and concentrates.

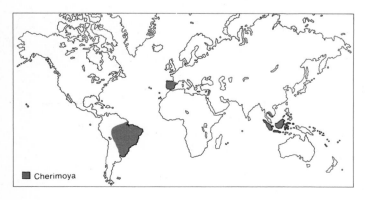

■ Cherimoya

△ Cherimoya, 4in (96mm) diameter ▽ Sugar Apple, 4in (96mm) diameter

Custard Apple or **Bullock's Heart** *(Annona recticulata)*
DESCRIPTION: An almost spherical fruit, 3½-5½in (7-12cm) across, with a lumpy surface. The skin of the ripe fruit is reddish-brown on a green background. The divisions between the parts of the composite fruit are less pronounced in this species. The creamy-white flesh is sweet and juicy, but also fibrous, and contains many inedible seeds.
COUNTRIES OF ORIGIN: Peru, Ecuador.

PRODUCER COUNTRIES: India, Kenya, Indonesia, Thailand, Florida.
AVAILABILITY: August to January.
USE: As cherimoya.
OTHER INFORMATION: As cherimoya.

Sugar Apple
(Annona squamosa)
DESCRIPTION: Green, heart-shaped fruit, approximately 4in (10cm) long and resembling a closed fir-cone due to its pronounced scales. When fully ripe it bursts open along the scales. The flesh is creamy-yellow in colour and has an exceptionally sweet taste.
COUNTRIES OF ORIGIN: Peru, Ecuador.
PRODUCER COUNTRY: Mainly Thailand.

AVAILABILITY: June to September.
USE: As cherimoya.
KEEPING QUALITIES: As cherimoya.
NUTRITIONAL VALUE: As cherimoya.
INDUSTRIAL PROCESSING: Not known.

19

Bombacaceae
Durian

The tropical family of the *Bombacaceae*, to which the monkey bread tree or baobab and the kapok tree also belong, produces only one species of fruit of more than local significance. This is the durian, a very large prickly fruit widely eaten in Southeast Asian countries, but only occasionally elsewhere. The main reason for this is its extremely unpleasant smell, especially when ripe. The durian is indigenous to Malaysia and Borneo, and is currently harvested on a commercial basis in various Southeast Asian countries. There are approximately ten varieties, including some that grow wild in the Malaysian primeval forest. The fruits develop on trees which can be 65-130ft (20-40m) high. The dark green, glossy leaves are golden-yellow or silver-coloured on the underside. The large, repugnantly scented, yellow flowers live for less than a day; they open in the afternoon and fall the following morning. The fruits are harvested unripe for export, are elongated or an irregular round shape and are thickly covered with stiff sharp thorns. They can weigh up to 6½lb (3kg). They are notorious for their penetrating odour — a mixture of old blue cheese, rotten onions or eggs, and turpentine. The smell is probably caused by sulphur compounds in the fruit.

Once removed from the skin, the yellowish white flesh smells less pungent. It has a creamy consistency and a taste which is a complicated mixture of banana and dried figs, with a hint of stewed onions, almonds and vanilla, and an aftertaste of garlic!

In Asia the 6-18 ochre-coloured seeds are eaten, usually roasted. In some countries where the plant is grown the flesh is dried or processed into a kind of pasta. Attempts to freeze-dry or preserve it in other ways have so far been unsuccessful.

As the durian can only be shipped by air (and because of its smell only in freight aircraft!), prices are quite high. The fruits are sold individually or by weight. After cutting, they must be eaten immediately. Whole fruits will keep for a few days.

△ Durian, 8½in (220mm) diameter

Durian
(Durio zibethinus)

DESCRIPTION: An elongated or irregular spherical fruit, 6-15in (15-35cm) long, 6-11in (15-25cm) across, and weighing up to 6lb (3kg). Olive-green skin changing to yellow and densely covered with sharp thorns up to ¾in (2cm) long. The flesh is yellowish-white or beige and contains 6-18 ochre-yellow seeds (in Asia mostly eaten roasted). It has a penetrating, very unpleasant odour that grows more pungent as it ripens. The flesh has a less penetrating smell. The taste is creamy and spicy, with an aftertaste reminiscent of vanilla.

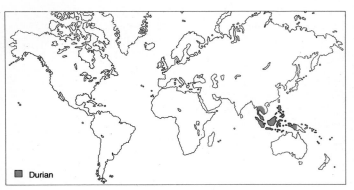

■ Durian

COUNTRIES OF ORIGIN: Malaysia, Borneo.

PRODUCER COUNTRIES: Thailand, Indonesia, Malaysia, Philippines.

AVAILABILITY: April to July.

USE: Scoop flesh out with a spoon or fork and eat fresh. Boil unripe fruits and mix into soup or vegetable dishes, or chop finely and mix with salt or vinegar. Incorporate into ice-cream. Roast or bake seeds in oil and eat with rice.

KEEPING QUALITIES: Undamaged fruits keep five to six days.

NUTRITIONAL VALUE: Rich in vitamins C, B1 and B3; rich in minerals; 143-179 Kcal per 100g serving.

INDUSTRIAL PROCESSING: Not known.

Bromeliaceae
Pineapple

The *Bromeliaceae* family has thousands of members, including many flowering tropical species that have become popular as greenhouse or indoor plants. The star of the family is the pineapple, eaten all over the world and grown in huge quantities in numerous countries. The pineapple originally came from what is now Paraguay and by the end of the 15th century, when the Spanish and Portuguese discovered the region, it was widely cultivated throughout Central America. This wide distribution was probably the work of the Guarani Indians who took the fruit with them on their voyages. The French name *ananas* is derived from the original Indian name *nana ment*, meaning 'exquisite fruit'. When the Spaniards sailing with Columbus saw the fruit in 1493 in Guadaloupe they nicknamed it *pina* as it resembled a fir-cone. And from this we get the name pineapple.

Around 1700 an Amsterdam merchant improved the pineapple by crossbreeding and sold cuttings to English growers who cultivated the fruit in greenhouses for the tables of the rich. Production under glass also took place in France, but died out during the 19th century when large-scale cultivation began in the Azores. In Hawaii cultivation had already started at the beginning of the 19th century, but until the arrival of modern transportation methods there were no exports to America or Europe. Until very recently pineapples sold in Europe came from the Azores. From 1945, the French encouraged pineapple cultivation in various African countries and now European supplies come mainly from the Ivory Coast, Kenya, Mali and South Africa.

Transport, in fact, is the greatest problem in marketing pineapples. In contrast to many other types of fruit, pineapples must ripen on the plant, enabling the sugars to form that give them their taste and aroma. Reliable post-harvest ripening is only possible to a limited extent, and so growers must ensure that the fruit is harvested as ripe as possible and transported immediately. Here again they are handicapped by the perishable nature of the pineapple. Completely ripe pineapples are impossible to ship, so they are now harvested when almost ripe and sent to their destination by air. Prime quality fruit is therefore expensive, and this has led to the development of varieties that keep better and so ship better.

A pineapple plant is usually about 2½ft (80cm) tall and consists of a rosette of long, narrow leaves. Older varieties have sharp thorns on their leaves which make harvesting difficult. However in recent years new thornless varieties have been developed. When the plant is between one and two years old, a woody flower spike grows out of the centre on which 100 or more flowers appear. Each flower produces a fruit and these fruits fuse together forming the scales of the rounded false fruit which is the pineapple we see in the shops. The crown of stiff, spiky leaves, if cut off together with a slice of the pineapple, will grow into a new pineapple plant.

The pineapple's scales tell us about its characteristics. The more marked the relief, the stronger the typical pineapple taste; the less marked the relief, the weaker the characteristic taste but the sweeter and juicier the flesh. When the scales have brown tips, the fruit is ripe. Ripe fruits are also soft to the touch at the opposite end to the crown. They have a characteristic pineapple smell and the smallest leaves of the crown closest to the fruit pull off easily.

Different pineapple varieties vary in colour. The greenish-yellow varieties are usually juicier than the orange-yellow ones which often have a stronger pineapple smell. Unripe pineapples will post-ripen at room temperature but this tends to dry them out.

About half of a pineapple consists of parts that you chop off and throw away. The leafy crown, the outer scales, the 'eyes' (which are the remains of the actual flowers) and the woody core (which is the stem of the plant), all have to be cut away, but some juice can still be squeezed out of the fleshy parts using a juice extractor. Like kiwi fruits and pawpaws, pineapples also contain an enzyme — in this case bromelin — which breaks down protein. So rubbing meat with pineapple or marinading it in pineapple juice tenderizes it and helps it to cook more quickly.

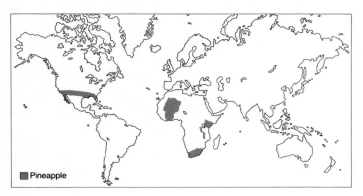

Pineapple

Pineapple
(Ananas comosus)

DESCRIPTION: A large, roundish false fruit that is actually made up of 100 or more true fruits, which are the 'scales' on the outside and the 'eyes' inside. Colour: greenish-yellow to orange-yellow, depending on the variety. The flesh is light to dark yellow in colour, and contains the woody remains of the flower stem. Between the outer shell of scales and the flesh there are cavities containing stiff, hard hairs, the 'eyes'. The flesh is sweet-tart, aromatic, and juicy when the fruit is ripe.

COUNTRY OF ORIGIN: Paraguay.

PRODUCER COUNTRIES: Ivory Coast, Kenya, Mali, South Africa, United States, Hawaii.

AVAILABILITY: Throughout the year from different producer countries.

USE: Slice off the leafy crown. Cut into slices and pare off the scaly edge and the core. Alternatively, cut the fruit lengthways into quarters. Remove the core and cut away the scaly skin, then slice the remaining flesh.
Pineapple is usually eaten raw, sometimes sprinkled with a little rum or topped with whipped cream. The fruit can also be cooked in meat and fish dishes and used in salads and desserts.

KEEPING QUALITIES: Very ripe fruit: two days at 56°F (8°C). Unripe fruit can be ripened more quickly by keeping it in a plastic bag at room temperature together with a ripe banana.

NUTRITIONAL VALUE: 55 Kcal, 20-100 i.u. vitamin A, and 30mg vitamin C per 100g serving.

INDUSTRIAL PROCESSING: Juice, canned in syrup, candied.

△ Smooth Cayenne, 6in (150mm) diameter

△ Sugar Loaf, 5in (127mm) across

Varieties

Alexandra Derived from 'Ripley Queen'. The round shape and the taste are the same, but the colour is golden-yellow turning to orange. The skin has pronounced scales.

Black Jamaica Looks similar to 'Sugar Loaf', but the very tasty flesh is dark yellow. 'Black Jamaica' is used extensively by growers for crossbreeding. Jamaica is the most important producer country.

Pernambuco A direct descendant of the pineapple variety brought to Europe by the Spaniards and Portuguese in the 15th century. It is a variety that does not keep well and is usually expensive because it has to be air-freighted. But it is well worth the money because it tastes excellent. The whitish-yellow flesh contains very fine fibres and is very juicy and sweet. Fruit breeders in Hawaii are now trying to cross 'Pernambuco' to improve its keeping qualities.

Red Spanish This variety is distinguished from others by its almost rectangular shape. The yellowish flesh is quite fibrous, with a pleasant, refreshingly sharp taste and a slight aroma. 'Red Spanish' comes mainly from Puerto Rico and travels well.

Ripley Queen The ripe fruit is golden-yellow and round, with pronounced bumpy scales. The flesh is deep yellow, rather dry and has a sharp pineapple aroma. The 'Queen' group includes: 'Z Queen', which is a little larger than 'Ripley' and comes mainly from South Africa; 'Egyptian Queen', which comes from all African producing countries; and 'Fairy Queen', from Australia and Malaysia, juicier than 'Ripley' but exported less frequently.

Smooth Cayenne A consumer favourite. The ripe fruit is dark orange-yellow on the outside and has a fairly smooth surface. The leaves are not thorny. Fruits that ripen in the hot season tend to have a darker colour. The flesh is yellow to dark yellow in colour and has a higher acid content than that of other species. The most important producing countries are the Ivory Coast, Kenya and South Africa.

Sugar Loaf A very heavy, round fruit, pointed at the top and weighing up to 10lb (4.5kg). The flesh is yellowish-white, sweet and very aromatic. A striking feature of this variety is that the fruit remains green for a very long time, even when it is ripe. In post-ripening it changes colour to yellowish-orange and develops a strong aroma. This variety is easily confused with 'Black Jamaica'. The most important producing countries are Mexico and Venezuela.

△ Pernambuco, 5in (123mm) diameter

25

Cactaceae
Prickly pear

The *Cactaceae* or cactus family has about 2,000 varieties ranging in height from ½in to 60ft (1cm to 18m). Nearly all of them are indigenous to the New World, with a heavier concentration in tropical and subtropical regions. Species belonging to only one genus *(Rhipalis)* are found in other parts of the world, namely tropical Africa and Sri Lanka, but even they may have come originally from the New World.

Cacti are stem succulents, in other words plants that can store moisture in their stems to help them survive long periods of drought. The stems are usually thickly covered with spines or hairs that protect the plant against being eaten by animals or birds and also against drying out. Some experts believe that the spines are modified leaves and there are, in fact, a few varieties that do have very small leaves.

Many species of cactus have spread from America to other tropical and subtropical regions. Many have become popular greenhouse and indoor plants. The intentional or accidental transfer of cacti to other parts of the world has not always been welcomed. In Australia, for example, where cacti are used for hedges, they spread and became a real menace until a special species of moth was imported to keep them under control.

The fruits of a number of cacti are edible. In tropical America, for instance, they are an important source of food for the local population. But only one of these edible fruits is eaten at all widely: the fruit of the cactus *Opuntia ficus indica,* the prickly pear or cactus fruit. Nowadays it is grown commercially in Italy, Spain and Israel.

The prickly pear plant can reach a height of 10ft (3m). Its disk-shaped 'leaves' bloom in spring, sprouting big yellow flowers from which large seed pods develop in summer and autumn. At first these are green in colour, but as they ripen they change through yellow and orange to light red and reddish-brown. Both the plant and the fruits are covered with very sharp spines; these are usually removed on harvesting, but the spine beds remain. These look like 'eyes' and are covered with thousands of tiny hairs which are barbed and break off easily. This is why prickly pears cannot be handled without gloves. If the

hairs get embedded in the skin, they cause irritation or inflammation and should be removed with tweezers or a piece of sticky tape. So gloves are a must! The fruit should, alternatively, be rubbed carefully with a cloth and then washed under the tap.

Prickly pears are very refreshing because they contain a lot of moisture. The flesh is like that of a watermelon in texture and has a slightly acid taste reminiscent of a pear. The pips are edible. Prickly pears are only really tasty when they are fully ripe, i.e. when they are orange. Some prickly pears have floury and very dry flesh. These should not be eaten. It is wise to eat prickly pears in moderation; they have a strong laxative effect! Five fruits per day is really the maximum.

The prickly pear cactus blooms in spring and in summer the fruits develop from the flowers. As they ripen they deepen in colour to a dark reddish-brown.

Prickly pear

△ Prickly Pear, 4in (10cm) long

Prickly Pear or **Cactus Fruit**
(Opuntia ficus indica)
DESCRIPTION: An oval fruit, 2½-4in (7-10cm) long. Changes colour as it ripens from green through yellow and orange to bright red and reddish-brown. The fruits are covered with small beds of tiny, vicious, barbed spines left where the large spines have been removed during harvesting. Like the watermelon, the flesh of the prickly pear contains a lot of water and also lots of edible pips. The taste is slightly acid.
COUNTRY OF ORIGIN: Mexico.

PRODUCER COUNTRIES: Italy, Israel, Spain, Morocco.
AVAILABILITY: July to February.
USE: Rub the fruits thoroughly with a cloth and rinse under the tap. Cut in half and scoop out flesh, or slice the top off and peel. Eat raw or use in fruit salads. Throw away floury fruits.
KEEPING QUALITIES: Ripe: a few days in the refrigerator.
NUTRITIONAL VALUE: 56 Kcal and 20mg vitamin C per 100g serving.
INDUSTRIAL PROCESSING: None.

Caricaceae

Pawpaw

The only fruit of the *Caricaceae* family that is widely known is the pawpaw or papaya *(Carica papaya)*, also called the tree melon. Related varieties such as the babao *(C. pentagona)* and the very sweet chamburo *(C. chrysopetala)* from Ecuador, and the mountain pawpaw *(C. candamarcensis)* from Columbia and Peru, are virtually unknown outside their own countries, although they figure largely in crossbreeding trials.

The Caricaceae family has only three genera and less than 50 species. The soft-stemmed trees have very few branches and are crowned with a topknot of green leaves under which the fruits grow in clusters. The exact origin of the pawpaw is not known. The Spaniards discovered the tree in tropical America in the 16th century and later introduced it into Asia. Now pawpaws are grown in many tropical and subtropical regions — in North and South America, Africa, Australia and Hawaii. Since crossbreeding started, many new varieties have been developed, some bearing very large fruits. Pawpaws for export vary in weight from 7oz (200g) to a maximum of 2lb (800g). They must be harvested almost ripe, when they are at their softest and most perishable. And because they cannot withstand low temperatures, refrigeration during shipment presents a problem.

Like the kiwi fruit and the pineapple, the pawpaw contains an enzyme that breaks down protein, in this case called papain, and is a useful meat tenderizer (see kiwi fruit under *Actinidiae*, page 10).

Differentiating between various species of pawpaw is not easy. But the differences largely concern not the consumer but the grower who has to consider commercial factors such as yield, suitability to climate and soil, resistance to disease, and so on. The consumer will hardly notice these differences because all varieties have very much the same taste, aroma and juiciness.

△ Hobson, 6in (155mm) long

Pawpaw
(Carica papaya)

DESCRIPTION: Greenish-yellow to deep orange fruit, up to 2in (5cm) long and similar in shape to a pear, a melon or an aubergine, depending on the variety. Ripe fruits have soft, juicy flesh and thin skin. Generally sweet-tasting, a bit like melon, with a slightly musky aroma. At the centre of the fruit there is a pocket filled with lots of small, greyish-black seeds. Ripe pawpaws are soft to the touch.

COUNTRIES OF ORIGIN: Central and South America.

PRODUCER COUNTRIES: South Africa, Ivory Coast, Thailand, Philippines, Australia, Hawaii, Brazil, Colombia, Mexico, United States.

AVAILABILITY: All year round from various producer countries.

USE: Eat ripe fruits like melon or make into jam, compote, desserts, etc. Unripe fruits can be eaten as vegetables, for example like courgettes.

KEEPING QUALITIES: Ripe fruits: one to two days at room temperature.

NUTRITIONAL VALUE: 39 Kcal, 2000-4000 i.u. vitamin A and 2mg vitamin C per 100g serving.

INDUSTRIAL PROCESSING: Jam and jelly, juice, dried, pickled, canned in syrup.

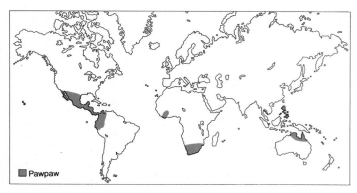

■ Pawpaw

Red Panama A Mexican variety ranging in colour from brownish green to brown when ripe. The flesh is pink or yellow and deliciously juicy. Sometimes the fruit is more round than oblong. Imported from Mexico, Texas and Colombia.

Solo An important variety extensively grown for export, and also the ancestor of many other popular varieties, such as 'Puna', 'Linie 8' and 'Linie 10', 'Hobson', 'Hortus Gold' and 'Honey Gold'. The skin is green, and the flesh orange or orange-yellow and very juicy.

Zamboanga A Philippine variety with more reddish-brown skin than other varieties. The flesh can be orange-yellow, and in some cases salmon pink.
The seeds are also larger than in other varieties — up to $\frac{1}{5}$in (5mm) across. In the Philippines the seeds are chewed or ground into a spice for seasoning food. The fruit is a little angular in shape. Unripe fruit has white flesh and can be eaten as a vegetable. The picture shows an unripe 'Zamboanga'.

△ Long Toms, 3in (280mm) long ▽ Zamboanga, 5in (120mm) diameter

Varieties

Hobson One of the varieties derived from 'Solo', mainly exported from South Africa. Like 'Solo', a greenish yellow skin and orange yellow flesh.

Long Toms From Queensland, Australia. Larger than other varieties; can be 16in (40cm) long and weigh 20lb (9kg).

29

Cucurbitaceae
Melon, watermelon, chayote, tindola

The extensive *Cucurbitaceae* or cucumber family comprises around 850 species belonging to approximately 100 genera. Almost all are climbing or creeping plants with heavy berry-like fruits. Apart from well known vegetables like the cucumber, gherkin and pumpkin, two other important fruit varieties belong to this family: the melon *(Cucumis melo)* and the watermelon *(Citrullus vulgaris or lanatus).*

Melon
The melon probably came from Central Asia, or possibly from Africa. The Greeks and Romans cultivated melons and it is said that Pope Paul II (1464-1471) died from eating too many. Today melons are grown in many tropical and subtropical regions as well as under glass in temperate climates.

Because melons are easy to crossbreed, there are a vast number of species and varieties. Melons are more than 90 per cent water. In the commercial fruit world melons are generally divided up into the following groups.
Cantaloupe melons. Named after a little town called Cantalupa near Rome, the fruits of this group are round or slightly flattened in shape. Sometimes the fruit surface is clearly divided into segments; sometimes the skin is covered with wart-like bumps. The orange or greenish flesh has an excellent flavour and a pleasant aroma. Cantaloupes do not keep very long. They are harvested almost ripe and must be eaten as soon as possible after buying. A typical example of this group is the French 'Charentais'.
Net melons. This group owes its name to the cork-like white or light brown network of fibres visible on the skin, which can be smooth or segmented in appearance. The flesh is usually apricot-coloured; taste and aroma vary depending on the species. A typical example is the 'Galia'.
Winter melons. These are also known as smooth, sugar or honey melons. The fruits are slightly elongated in shape and the skin is smooth or grooved. Fruits of this group generally ripen late and are mostly imported in the winter months. Because of their hard skin they can sometimes be kept for a month or longer. Taste and aroma are generally blander than those of the other groups. The white or yellow, smooth or grooved 'Honeydew' melon, grown mainly in Spain, is a good example.
Ogen melons. 'Ogen' is the name of the Israeli kibbutz where these melons were first grown. Ogens are small and look a little like Cantaloupe-type melons. They are orange-yellow in colour and have a grooved skin. The flesh is light green and quite delicious. When ripe an Ogen has a strong aroma and feels soft at the end opposite to the stalk, and the stalk — if present — comes away easily.

Most varieties post-ripen at room temperature, i.e. 60-70°F (15-20°C), and, depending on their ripeness, can be kept for five to eight days. At temperatures below 47°F (8°C) watery mould spots develop in the skin and flesh. All melons should be eaten chilled for the flavour and aroma to be at their best.

Watermelon
The watermelon comes from North Africa and India and nowadays is grown in many other tropical and subtropical countries. It is popular in hot countries because it is very watery and thirst-quenching. It has almost no aroma, but a sweetish taste which breeders are still trying to improve.

Most watermelons for export are round, dark green in colour and weigh a few pounds. There are one or two elongated species which have a light or dark green marbled skin; these can be very large indeed, weighing up to 45lb (20kg)! Such giants are less in demand simply because they are too large for the family table. When they do appear on the market, they are often sold in sections.

The flesh of a watermelon is pink to deep red in colour, and crisp. The numerous flat brownish-black seeds are randomly dispersed throughout the flesh. In some countries these are roasted and eaten salted; in Indonesia, for example, they are used to make a delicacy called *kwatji.* The flesh can be slightly insipid, but usually the riper the fruit, the sweeter the taste.

It is difficult to determine whether a watermelon is ripe or not. The best method is to tap the fruit. The duller the sound, the riper the fruit; unripe watermelons sound faintly metallic.

Watermelon exporters are the Mediterranean countries, the United States and Mexico. A watermelon will keep at room temperature for several weeks. Once cut it can be kept in the refrigerator for a few days, wrapped in plastic film. Like other melons, watermelons cannot be stored at temperatures below 47°F (8°C).

■ Melon

Melon
(Cucumis melo)

DESCRIPTION: Round, elongated or slightly flattened, up to 12in (30cm) long. Can have smooth, grooved, ribbed or netted skin, yellow, white, orange, greenish or greyish-ochre in colour, depending on the variety. The flesh, too, varies in colour: orange, greenish, white, yellow or pink. Taste and aroma also vary widely. At the centre of the fruit is a moisture-filled cavity full of pips.

COUNTRY OF ORIGIN: Probably Central Asia.

PRODUCER COUNTRIES: France, Spain, Italy, Israel, Mali, Brazil, Chile, South Africa, Greece, United States.

AVAILABILITY: All year round from various producer countries.

USE: Cut in half and remove pips and fibres. Scoop out the flesh or slice and cut flesh away from the skin. Eat raw or use in appetizers, fruit salads, desserts, or fish and poultry dishes.

KEEPING QUALITIES: Unripe fruits post-ripen at room temperature and can be kept for about a week; ripe fruits must be eaten as soon as possible. Do not store below 47°F (8°C).

NUTRITIONAL VALUE: 26 Kcal, 500 i.u. vitamin A, 5-10mg vitamin C, and a little vitamin B per 100g serving.

INDUSTRIAL PROCESSING: Canned in syrup, canned fruit cocktail, juice, candied.

Varieties

Honey Melon or **Yellow Honey Melon** An oval fruit, yellow in colour, with deep, longitudinal grooves in the skin. The flesh is light green to yellow in colour, juicy and tasty. Belongs to the winter melon group.

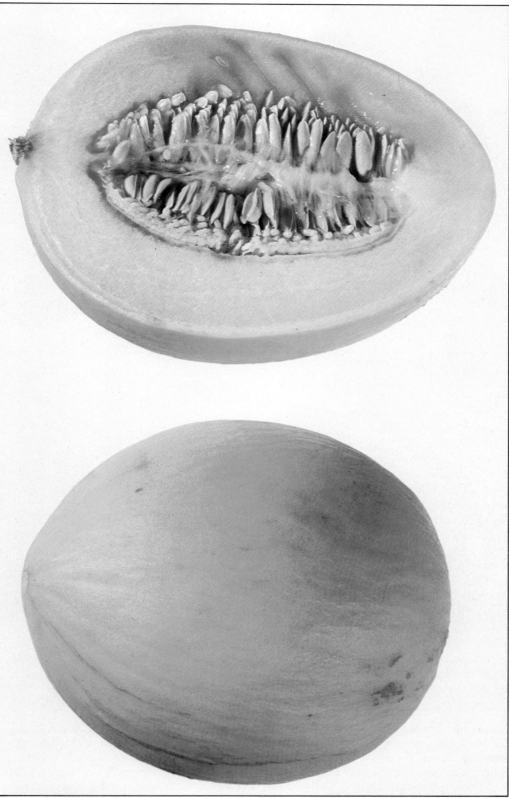

△ Honey Melon, 5¼in (135mm) long

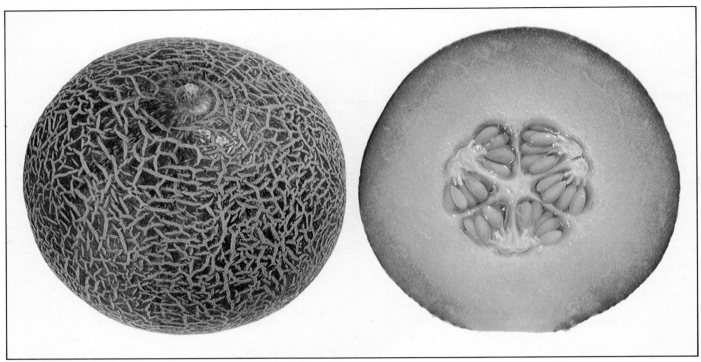

△ Galia, 5in (129mm) diameter   ▽ Dutch Net Melon, 6in (146mm) diameter

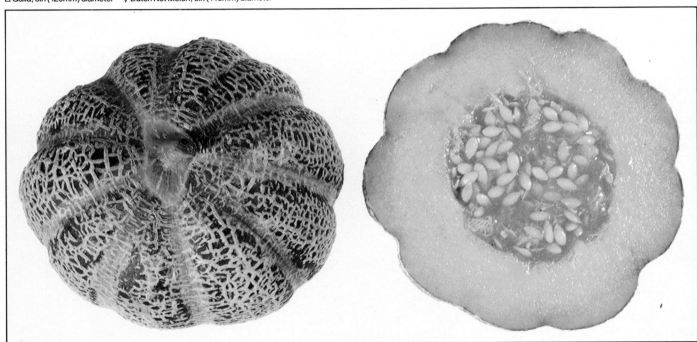

Charentais A melon of the Cantaloupe group grown mainly in France. The skin is light green to cream in colour, with shallow segments. The fruit usually has a rather flattened shape. The flesh is orange, very juicy and delicious. Does not keep long and should be eaten as soon as it is bought. Available from March to October.

Elche A green, smooth winter melon, imported in December and January mostly from South Africa and sometimes from Spain. Like most winter melons the taste is a little insipid.

Galia Named after the daughter of the Israeli grower who first developed it. Available since 1976. Initially it was grown only in Israel but now also comes from Spain and Italy. 'Galia' is yellowish-green in colour and has a deeply segmented skin. The flesh is light green and has an excellent taste and aroma. Available March to December.

Dutch Net Melon A flattish, round fruit, with a light netted skin and deeply indented segments. The very juicy flesh is light orange and tastes rather insipid. Now grown less extensively under glass because of the arrival of tastier varieties. Available June to September.

△ Honeydew, 7in (168mm) long ▽ Charentais, 4in (99mm) diameter

Honeydew An important variety belonging to the winter melon group. White or creamy in colour, with a smooth skin. The flesh is orange or light green and has a good taste, although not much aroma. Imported from Israel, South Africa, Italy and United States, where the variety was introduced at the beginning of the century from France. Ancestor of the new variety 'Floridew', recognizable by its slimmer shape and the slight segmenting of the skin. Available August to April.

Musk Melon The ripe fruit has a musky fragrance, hence the name. It is round or oval in shape and has a green skin, with dense, grey netting on the segments. The very juicy flesh is delicious. Originally from Italy but now grown chiefly in South Africa, Brazil, Chile and United States.

△ Ogen, 4½in (115mm) diameter

Ogen This almost round fruit takes its name from the Israeli kibbutz where the fruit was first grown. Greenish-yellow in colour, it has a smooth skin with shallow segments. The ripe fruits have a strong fragrance, and the flesh is juicy and light green in colour. Available April to January. Exported from Israel, France and Spain.

Orange Pineapple or **Tiger Pineapple** A round, segmented and creamy-coloured fruit with green blotches. Changes to orange when ripe. The flesh is orange, firm and juicy, with an excellent flavour. Grown under glass in the Netherlands and Germany. Available June to October.

Persian or **Round Net Melon** A dark green melon with a dense, grey network on the skin and firm orange-coloured flesh full of flavour. Available February to August and mainly exported from Italy and Greece.

Tendral This oval-shaped variety is also called 'Black Tendral' or 'Late Tendral'. Belongs to the winter melon group. The skin is dark green and grooved. The yellowish-green flesh has little taste and is best used in fruit salads or served with sliced ham as an hors d'oeuvre. 'Tendral' can be kept for quite a long time (up to five weeks) because of its hard skin. Available September to April. Exported from Spain, Brazil and Chile.

34

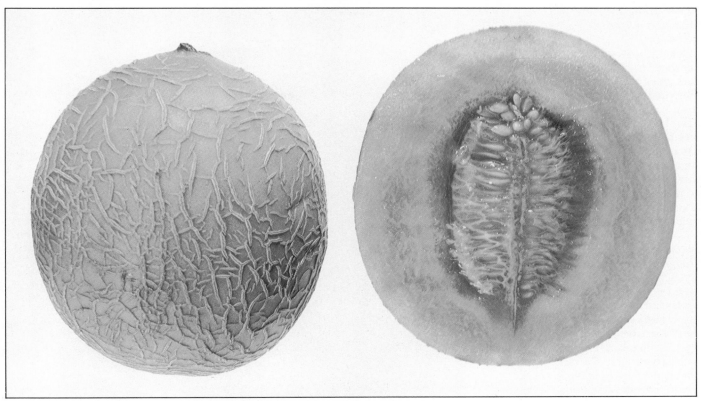

△ White Sugar Melon, 6½in (167mm) long   Orange Pineapple, 7in (172mm) long

White Sugar Melon A smooth, white, round fruit that changes colour to yellow when ripe. The flesh is light green and tastes very sweet (sugar content can be high as 15 per cent). Grown extensively under glass in the Netherlands.

Watermelon
(Citrullus vulgaris; C. lanatus)

DESCRIPTION: Round or elongated fruit with a smooth dark green or dark and light green marbled skin. Weighs from 5 or 6lb (2 or 3kg) to over 33lb (15kg). The flesh is light pink to dark red in colour and has a crunchy texture, with large, dark brown seeds scattered through it. Almost no aroma and a sweetish taste.

COUNTRIES OF ORIGIN: Africa, India.

PRODUCER COUNTRIES: Italy, Spain, Greece, France, Hungary, Cyprus, United States, Mexico.

AVAILABILITY: All year round but less in the winter months.

USE: Usually eaten raw as a thirst-quencher. Can also be used in fruit salads (together with tastier fruits). The taste can be enhanced by adding wine or liqueur and serving chilled.

KEEPING QUALITIES: Up to ten days at room temperature, depending on ripeness. Cut fruits wrapped in plastic film can be kept for a few days in the salad drawer of the refrigerator.

NUTRITIONAL VALUE: 23 Kcal, 590 i.u. vitamin A, 7mg vitamin C, and traces of vitamin B per 100g serving.

INDUSTRIAL PROCESSING: None.

△ Crimson, 11in (276mm) diameter

Varieties

Black Diamond Also called 'Cannon Ball' or 'Florida Giant'. Very large, dark green watermelon weighing as much as 40lb (18kg). The flesh is dark red in colour, crunchy, and quite sweet.

Charleston Gray A large, elongated fruit, greyish-green in colour with green stripes or blotches and sometimes weighing up to 44lb (20kg). Travels well because the skin is thin but hard. Available throughout the year.

Crimson Looks like its close relative 'Charleston Gray'. Sweet and has few pips in the light red or pink flesh. It travels extremely well and is available throughout the year.

Klondike Striped A relatively small, yellowish-green, marbled watermelon with a firm skin and magenta flesh that tastes and smells sweet. This variety travels well. 'Klondike' crosses include 'Peacock' and 'Blue Riband Klondike' and are hard to distinguish from 'Klondike Striped'. Available all year round.

△ Sugar Baby, 9in (220mm) diameter

Miyako A light green round fruit with dark marbled spots, weighing up to 11lb (5kg). The flesh is light red, crunchy and sweet. 'Miyako' was developed in Japan but is grown mainly in Italy. Available June to end October.

New Hampshire Midget A round, dark green fruit with deep red, sweet flesh, very similar to 'Sugar Baby'. An American variety only sporadically exported to Europe.

Sugar Baby One of the earliest and most popular of all watermelons, with light red, sweet flesh containing lots of black pips. 'Sweety', a close relative of 'Sugar Baby', has fewer pips and is sweeter. 'Sugar Baby' comes chiefly from Italy, Greece and Israel. Available May to October.

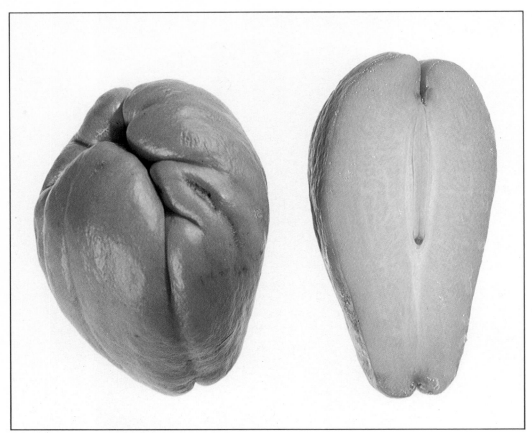

halved and cooked fruits, mix the flesh with grated gherkin or pickled cucumber, mayonnaise, tomato ketchup and flakes of crab or lobster and put mixture back into skins. Serve cold or bake in the oven. As a dessert: cook slices in a little water and sugar and mix with other fruits.
KEEPING QUALITIES: Unripe fruits keep for weeks and sometimes months at refrigerator temperature.
NUTRITIONAL VALUE: 30 Kcal and 20mg vitamin C per 100g serving.
INDUSTRIAL PROCESSING: None.

Tindola or **Papasan**
(Coccinia cordifolia)
DESCRIPTION: A small fruit with a smooth skin, 1½-2½in (3-6cm) long. As it ripens, the fruit changes colour from green to orange to deep red.
COUNTRY OF ORIGIN: Southeast Asia.
PRODUCER COUNTRIES: Asia, Africa.
AVAILABILITY: Throughout the year.
USE: Eat as cucumber, or boil or roast with vegetables.
KEEPING QUALITIES: Up to ten days in the refrigerator.
NUTRITIONAL VALUE: Not known.
INDUSTRIAL PROCESSING: None.

△ Chayote, 3⅝in (91mm) long   ▽ Tindola, 1½-2in (42-46mm) diameter

Chayote or **Laboe Siam**
(Sechium edule)
DESCRIPTION: Yellowish-green, pear-shaped fruit weighing up to 1lb 2oz (500g). It has a wrinkled, somewhat scabby skin and the whitish flesh has a sweet, watery taste rather like a combination of cucumber and courgette. There is a large edible pip, which becomes inedible as it hardens.
COUNTRY OF ORIGIN: South America.
PRODUCER COUNTRIES: Tropical America (Guatemala, Honduras), Algeria, Indonesia, Hawaii, Philippines.
AVAILABILITY: August to March.
USE: It is best to peel chayotes under running water, as they are slimy and not easy to handle, then slice and sprinkle with salt and lemon juice. The slices can be cooked and served with ham, curries or in a cheese sauce. Can also be served as a vegetable, mixed with carrots or tomatoes, for example. Alternatively, hollow out the

Ebenaceae
Persimmon

The *Ebenaceae* family contains approximately 400 species and is not renowned for its fruit. Of the five edible fruits in this group, there are four which up until now have only been locally available and seldom, if ever, exported. They are the lotus fruit *(Diospyros lotus)*, indigenous to Asia, bluish-black in colour, roughly the same size as a cherry and with a floury texture; the mabolo *(Diospyros discolor);* the black zapote *(D. ebenaster);* and the equally floury North American persimmon *(D. virginiana).* This last species was probably introduced from Southeast Asia in the 16th century.

The fifth edible species in the family is now becoming popular: it is the persimmon, which originally came from China and Japan. It grows on quite a tall deciduous tree and has the shape, size and colour of a tomato, with a four-leaved calyx where the stalk joins the fruit. The calyx leaves often look rather withered.

One characteristic of the persimmon is its high tannic acid (tannin) content. This disappears when the fruit is completely ripe or, better, over-ripe. Before this stage, the sweet and rather aromatic flavour is completely masked by a bitter, harsh taste that makes the tongue and palate contract unpleasantly. Because ripe persimmons are so soft they go off very quickly. This is why they are harvested and shipped well before they are ripe. This means that the fruit is sold unripe and the consumer has to ripen it at home. The process can be speeded up by putting the fruit in a plastic bag together with other ripe fruits, such as apples, pears, bananas or tomatoes. The ethylene gas given off by the ripe fruit accelerates the ripening of the persimmons.

Persimmons are now grown in many sub-tropical countries and growers have succeeded in developing several different varieties. One is the Israeli 'Sharon fruit', a variety which has had all trace of seeds, core and tannin bred out of it. This variety can be eaten unripe when the flesh is still firm. Unripe it eats just like an apple.

Persimmons have a very high vitamin A content, which makes them not only suitable as baby food but also a useful cure for hangovers!

△ Persimmon, 3in (80mm) diameter

Persimmon
(Diospyros kaki)

DESCRIPTION: Round, elongated fruit, shaped like a top, up to 4in (10cm) across. Varieties vary in colour from yellow to dark orange and may have a grooved skin. Inside, the fruit is divided into compartments filled with soft flesh and a varying number of pips, which are absent altogether in some varieties. The taste is essentially sweet, sometimes with a banana or vanilla aroma. Unripe fruits taste unpleasantly rough and bitter; only the Israeli 'Sharon fruit' is the exception.

COUNTRIES OF ORIGIN: Japan, China.

PRODUCER COUNTRIES: France, Italy, Israel, Spain, South Africa, Brazil, United States.

AVAILABILITY: Throughout the year from various producer countries.

USE: Eat very ripe fruits fresh and unpeeled, or slice into fruit salads and desserts.

KEEPING QUALITIES: A few days at room temperature.

NUTRITIONAL VALUE: 77 Kcal, 2710 i.u. vitamin A and 11mg vitamin C per 100g serving.

INDUSTRIAL PROCESSING: Into syrup or alcohol, preserves, frozen.

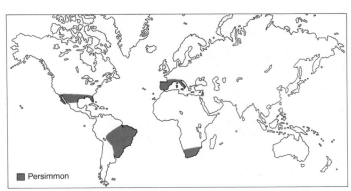

■ Persimmon

Ericaceae
Blueberry, cranberry, arbutus berry,
bilberry, huckleberry, whortleberry

The *Ericaceae* or heather family comprises not only hardy moorland heathers but also rhododendrons and azaleas. In origin almost all *Ericaceae* species are dwarf bushes that grow on acid soils in temperate climates.

The genus *Vaccinium* (bilberry) comprises a fair number of species which bear edible fruits, picked and eaten since time immemorial, especially by nomadic peoples, as an important source of food and vitamins.

These berries are still gathered in many places, especially in Europe; in summer and autumn, picking bilberries and whortleberries is a popular pastime, though rather time-consuming. Two species are grown on a commercial basis in Europe, namely the blueberry *(Vaccinium corymbosum)* and the cranberry *(Vaccinium macrocarpum)*.

The blueberry has been extensively used for crossbreeding purposes and came originally from North America. It is not an improved bilberry, as some people contend. The blueberry is a different species, and tastes different too; it also has a colourless juice whereas the juice of the bilberry is deep purple. The blueberry is also much larger, up to 1in (2.5cm) across. It grows in clusters on bushes up to 13ft (4m) tall and can be harvested by machine.

The cranberry is of North American origin, although it also grows in Western Europe. Virtually all imports into Europe come from the United States.

The fruits of the arbutus or strawberry tree are rare outside Mediterranean countries, but are occasionally exported in small quantities. Arbutus berries are round and taste rather tart.

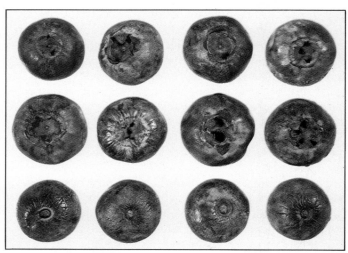

△ Blueberry, ⅝in (16mm) diameter

Blueberry
(Vaccinium corymbosum)
DESCRIPTION: Dark blue berries with a smooth skin, ½-1in (1.5-2.5cm) across. Apart from their size and their pleasanter taste, blueberries are distinguishable from bilberries by their colourless juice. Blueberries grow in clusters on quite tall bushes.
COUNTRY OF ORIGIN: North America.
PRODUCER COUNTRIES: United States, Netherlands, Germany, Belgium.
AVAILABILITY: July to September.
USE: Eat fresh or process into jam, compote, juice, etc. Also suitable for fruit salads, flan fillings, etc.
KEEPING QUALITIES: At room temperature two days; at 39-41°F (4-5°C) maximum ten days.
NUTRITIONAL VALUE: 81 i.u. vitamin A, 2.5mg vitamin C, and a little vitamin B per 100g serving.
INDUSTRIAL PROCESSING: Jam, compote, jelly, juice.

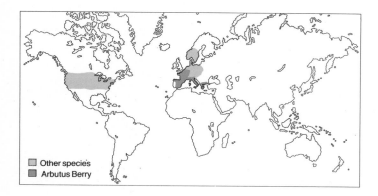

☐ Other species
◼ Arbutus Berry

△ Large Cranberry, ⅝in (16mm) diameter

Large Cranberry
(Vaccinium macrocarpum)
DESCRIPTION: The dark to light
red fruits are ½-1in (8-25mm)
across, depending on the
species and variety. The taste is
tart and slightly bitter; the skin
sometimes has a very sharp
taste, especially when the fruits
are under-ripe.
COUNTRY OF ORIGIN: North
America, Northern Asia.
PRODUCER COUNTRIES: United
States, Germany, Scandinavia.
AVAILABILITY: October to April.
USE: Eat fresh or boil for five
minutes and make into
compote, either by itself or
mixed with apple or pear; a
good accompaniment to meat
and poultry. Can be spiced
with vanilla, cinnamon, red
wine or grated orange peel.

KEEPING QUALITIES: Several
months at 34-37°F (1-3°C).
Deep frozen: virtually
unlimited. In packaged form at
room temperature: at least a
few weeks.
NUTRITIONAL VALUE: 52 Kcal
and 30-40g vitamin C per 100g
serving.
INDUSTRIAL PROCESSING: Juice,
compote, wine.

Arbutus Berry
(Arbutus unedo)
DESCRIPTION: The fruits of the
strawberry tree, which grows
to 30ft (9m) tall, are
approximately ½in (2cm) across,
grow in clusters at the branch
tips and have the appearance of
lychees. They have a hard,
knobbly skin that is initially
yellow but changes to orange-
brown as it ripens. The flesh is
yellow, acid to the taste and has
no aroma.
COUNTRIES OF ORIGIN:
Mediterranean countries.
PRODUCER COUNTRIES: France,
Italy, Spain, Greece.
AVAILABILITY: September to
October.
USE: Peel and make into liqueur,
jam or compote.

KEEPING QUALITIES: A few days.
NUTRITIONAL VALUE: Not
known.
INDUSTRIAL PROCESSING: Liqueur
(in southern France).

Bilberry or Huckleberry
(Vaccinium myrtillus)

DESCRIPTION: Small, dull blue berries with deep purple flesh and juice. The taste is sweet and very pleasant. The berries grow individually under the leaves, making picking a time-consuming business.

COUNTRIES OF ORIGIN: Northern Europe and Asia.

PRODUCER COUNTRIES: Poland, Netherlands, Germany.

AVAILABILITY: August to October.

USE: Eat fresh or make into juice, jam or compote. The juice is good for stomach and bowel disorders.

KEEPING QUALITIES: A few days.

NUTRITIONAL VALUE: 51 Kcal, 81 i.u. vitamin A, 2.4mg vitamin C, and many minerals per 100g serving.

INDUSTRIAL PROCESSING: Jam, compote, juice.

△ Bilberry or Huckleberry, ¼in (6.5mm) diameter ▽ Red Whortleberry, ¼in (6.5mm) diameter

Bog Whortleberry
(Vaccinium uliginosum)

DESCRIPTION: Blue, oval berry that grows in groups of two or three. The flesh is white, the juice colourless. Tastes sweetish. Eaten to excess, can have an intoxicating effect resulting in headache and nausea.

COUNTRIES OF ORIGIN: Northern Europe.

PRODUCER COUNTRIES: Germany, some East European countries.

AVAILABILITY: August to September.

USE: Make into jam, juice or jelly.

KEEPING QUALITIES: A few days.

NUTRITIONAL VALUE: Not known.

INDUSTRIAL PROCESSING: None.

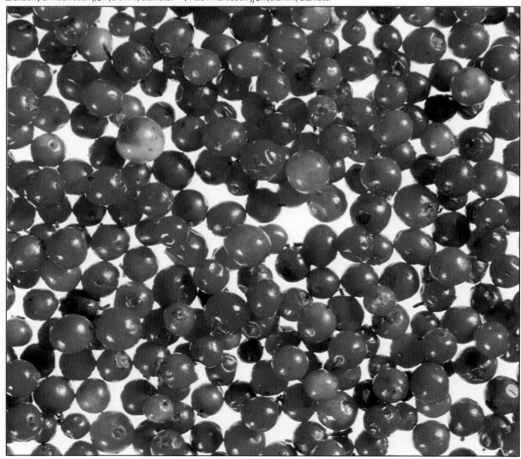

△ Small Cranberry, ½in (10mm) diameter

Red Whortleberry
(Vaccinium vitis idaea)
DESCRIPTION: The light red,
round berries grow in clusters
on the stem tops of an
evergreen plant. They taste best
after the first night frosts. Both
raw and cooked, they are an
appetite stimulant. Berries are $\frac{5}{32}$
to $\frac{5}{16}$in (4-8mm) across.
COUNTRIES OF ORIGIN: Northern
and Central Europe.
PRODUCER COUNTRIES:
Germany, Scandinavia, Poland,
Austria.
AVAILABILITY: July to October.
USE: Make into compote, jam,
jelly and juice.

KEEPING QUALITIES: A few
weeks.
NUTRITIONAL VALUE: 12mg
vitamin C per 100g serving.
INDUSTRIAL PROCESSING:
Canned in syrup, juice,
compote.

Small Cranberry
(Vaccinium oxycoccus)
DESCRIPTION: The round berries
change from pale yellow to
deep red as they ripen. The
taste is pleasantly acid when
fully ripe but can become bitter
after processing.
COUNTRIES OF ORIGIN: North
America and Northern Asia.
PRODUCER COUNTRIES:
Germany, Scandinavia, United
States.
AVAILABILITY: September to
December.
USE: Chiefly made into
compote and jelly as
acccompaniment to
meat and poultry.

KEEPING QUALITIES: A few days.
NUTRITIONAL VALUE: As red
whortleberry.
INDUSTRIAL PROCESSING: Jelly
and compote (canned or in
glass jars), sometimes frozen.

Flacourtiaceae
Kei apple, Ceylon gooseberry, ramontschi, batako plum, melindjo

The few edible fruits of the *Flacourtiaceae* are only used in oriental cooking. They can be eaten fresh, but are much more frequently made into side dishes, especially for the Indonesian rice table. If they are on sale at all elsewhere, it is in specialized ethnic food shops. Breeding experiments are now going on, especially with the ramontschi and the kei apple, to develop varieties that might be viable on the international market

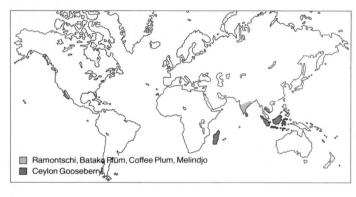

Ramontschi, Batako Plum, Coffee Plum, Melindjo
Ceylon Gooseberry

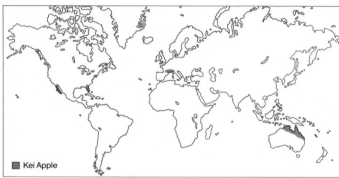

Kei Apple

Kei Apple
(Aberia caffra)
DESCRIPTION: Round fruit, $\frac{1}{2}$-$1\frac{1}{2}$in (1-4cm) in diameter and with a little crown on the underside. The thin skin is golden-yellow, the juicy, refreshingly sharp flesh whitish-yellow. The fruits contain 5-15 small, flat pips.
COUNTRY OF ORIGIN: South Africa.
PRODUCER COUNTRIES: France, Australia, United States (California and Florida).
AVAILABILITY: Throughout the year.
USE: Eat fresh or make into jam or jelly.

Ceylon Gooseberry
(Aberia gardneri)
DESCRIPTION: Round, purple fruit, $\frac{1}{2}$-$1\frac{1}{2}$in (1-4cm) in diameter, with a velvety skin. The flesh is dark red, juicy and sweet, and smells like ripe gooseberries. But the skin is bitter.
COUNTRY OF ORIGIN: Sri Lanka.
PRODUCER COUNTRIES: Sri Lanka, India, United States (California and Florida).
AVAILABILITY: Throughout the year.
USE: Peel and eat fresh or make into jam.

Batako Plum
(Flacourtia inermis)
DESCRIPTION: A round fruit $\frac{1}{2}$-$1\frac{1}{2}$in (1-4cm) in diameter, changing colour from greenish-yellow to purple as it ripens. The taste of the ripe fruit is refreshingly sharp. Unripe fruits are often made into pickle which can be eaten cold or hot.
COUNTRY OF ORIGIN: Indonesia.
PRODUCER COUNTRIES: Indonesia, Madagascar.
AVAILABILITY: October to February.
USE: Eat fresh or make into pickle.

Ramontschi
(Flacourtia indica)
DESCRIPTION: Round fruit with a small crown on the underside. Diameter $\frac{1}{2}$-$1\frac{1}{2}$in (2-4cm). The thin skin is dark brown, and the creamy-coloured flesh varies in taste from acid to sweet and fragrant.
COUNTRY OF ORIGIN: Malaysia, Madagascar.
PRODUCER COUNTRIES: Thailand, Madagascar, Indonesia.
AVAILABILITY: Throughout the year.
USE: Eat fresh or make into jam or jelly.
KEEPING QUALITIES: Not known, probably very short.
NUTRITIONAL VALUE: Not known.
INDUSTRIAL PROCESSING: None.

Coffee Plum
(Flacourtia rukam)
DESCRIPTION: Dark red, round fruit, about 1in (2.5cm) in diameter and similar in structure to the ramontschi. The white flesh tastes sour-sweet and contains many small pips.
COUNTRY OF ORIGIN: Indonesia, Madagascar.
PRODUCER COUNTRIES: Sri Lanka, Indonesia.
AVAILABILITY: Throughout the year, especially October to January.
USE: As ramontschi.

Melindjo
(Gnetum gnemon)
DESCRIPTION: Round fruit, $\frac{1}{2}$-$1\frac{1}{2}$in (2-4cm) in diameter. It changes colour from green through yellow to red as it ripens. The fruit consists of little more than the skin and a hard pip. The whole fruit is boiled, dried and then flattened into a kind of pancake known as melindjo pancake or *emping*. Emping is used, boiled in oil, in oriental cooking.
COUNTRY OF ORIGIN: Southeast Asia.
PRODUCER COUNTRIES: Japan, Indonesia, Thailand, China.

△ Melindjo, ⅞in (20mm) diameter

Guttiferae
Mangosteen, mundu, San Domingo apricot, madroño

Some botanists prefer to sub-divide the *Guttiferae* into two separate families: the generally tropical and sub-tropical *Clusiaceae* family and the *Hypericaceae* family, some species of which also grown in Northern Europe, for example St. John's wort *(Hypericum perforatum)*.

The most important fruiting genus is *Garcinia*, with around 180 species found in Asia and Africa. But only two fruits from this genus are well known: the Indonesian mundu and the mangosteen. The latter is so delicious that it is often called the 'queen of fruits'.

The mangosteen grows throughout Southeast Asia on bushy trees that can grow to 80ft (25m). Mangosteens present difficulties with harvesting, not only because the trees take ten to fifteen years to bear fruit (eight or nine for trees grafted onto wild *Garcinia* stock) but also because they are very choosy about the climates and soils they will grow in. Outside Asia, the mangosteen has been cultivated in Central America and Brazil, but only in very limited areas. The fruits are usually expensive.

Mangosteens are mostly sold in bunches tied together with raffia. Fruits with four or eight distinct marks on the underside are rare — more usually there are five, six or seven. In Indonesia fruits with four or eight marks are thought to bring good luck, just like our four-leaved clover. The skin contains a lot of tannin and the juice is also used in the Far East for curing leather and as ink.

One *Guttifera* species that will probably become much more familiar in the next few years is the San Domingo apricot from South and Central America. It has been the subject of trials in Florida since the fifties. A few improved varieties have already been produced, though they have not yet been marketed under individual variety names, so size, taste and smell still vary widely. On Martinique, a liqueur called 'Eau de Créole' or 'Crème de Créole' is distilled from the blossom of the 50-80ft (15-25m) tall trees.

The madroño is a South American fruit, virtually unknown in Europe, and very seldom imported, mainly because its uses are rather limited.

△ Mangosteen, 1½in (43mm) diameter

Mangosteen
(Garcinia mangostana)

DESCRIPTION: A purple, almost spherical fruit, 1½-3in (4-8cm) in diameter, usually with four neat sepals around the stalk. On the underside of the fruit there are four to eight distinct marks. Beneath the ½in (1cm) thick skin, the syrupy flesh is divided into sections, the number of which generally coincides with the number of marks on the underside of the fruit. The flesh is waxy white in colour and sometimes contains two pips in each section. It is refreshingly sweet and has a fragrance not unlike that of a grape or a peach.

COUNTRY OF ORIGIN: Malaysia.

PRODUCER COUNTRIES: Thailand, Indonesia, Central America, Brazil.

AVAILABILITY: Throughout the year.

USE: Peel the skin and eat the flesh raw or use in fruit salads or desserts with ice-cream or whipped cream.

KEEPING QUALITIES: In the refrigerator, one week; at room temperature, a few days. Mangosteens are sold ripe because they do not ripen once they are picked. The flesh of fruit that has gone off is brown and watery.

NUTRITIONAL VALUE: High in vitamin C.

INDUSTRIAL PROCESSING: Canned.

Mundu
(Garcinia dulcis)

DESCRIPTION: Slightly pear-shaped, approximately 2in (5cm) across. Yellow or brown fruit with a refreshingly sweet, piquant taste.

COUNTRY OF ORIGIN: Indonesia.

PRODUCER COUNTRY: Indonesia.

AVAILABILITY: August to October.

USE: Peel and eat raw or use in fruit salads or desserts. Fruits that are too acid can be made into jam or jelly.

KEEPING QUALITIES: As mangosteen.

NUTRITIONAL VALUE: High in vitamin C.

INDUSTRIAL PROCESSING: None.

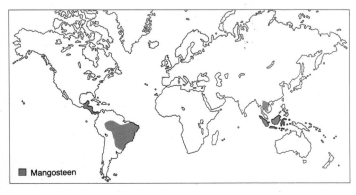

■ Mangosteen

San Domingo Apricot
(Mammea americana)

DESCRIPTION: Round fruit, 4-6in (10-15cm) in diameter and with a light to dark brown, rather rough and thick skin. The yellow or creamy flesh is sour-sweet to the taste and very fragrant. Depending on variety and ripeness, tastes a bit like an apricot (when sweet and juicy) or a cooking apple (when sour and hard). The fruit contains up to four long oval pips.

COUNTRIES OF ORIGIN: Central and South America.

PRODUCER COUNTRIES: Brazil, Colombia, Venezuela.

AVAILABILITY: June to September.

USE: Peel and eat raw, use in fruit salads, or simmer with sugar to make compote. With certain varieties, cooking brings out the apricot taste.

KEEPING QUALITIES: About two weeks in the refrigerator.

NUTRITIONAL VALUE: Not known.

INDUSTRIAL PROCESSING: None.

Madroño
(Rheedia madruno)

DESCRIPTION: Yellow, almost round fruit, approximately 4in (10cm) in diameter and with a hard skin a bit like that of a lychee. The fruit contains two to five large pips. What flesh there is tastes acid and has practically no aroma.

COUNTRY OF ORIGIN: South America.

PRODUCER COUNTRIES: Some South American countries (the madroño is really semi-wild rather than cultivated).

AVAILABILITY: Autumn (very sporadically).

△ San Domingo Apricot, 5in (125mm) across

Lauraceae
Avocado pear

One member of the *Lauraceae* family, the laurel *(Laurus nobilis),* grows in sub-tropical regions and in Europe but the rest of the family is mainly tropical. Aromatic products from this family include camphor and cinnamon. The only edible fruit produced by the *Lauraceae* family is the avocado pear, which can be eaten as a vegetable or a fruit. Avocado pears grow on trees that can reach a height of 65ft (20m), and came originally from tropical South and Central America. Cultivated varieties are often grafted onto wild stock. All avocados on the market today are cultivated varieties and come from many producer countries. The height of cultivated trees is restricted for easier harvesting.

There are literally hundreds of different varieties of avocado, generally sub-divided into three types.

Mexican type. Slender, pear-shaped fruits with a light green colour and an almost smooth skin.

Guatemalan type. Compact, spherical fruits with a smooth, green skin or with a purple or black, leathery and warty skin, the so-called alligator type.

West Indian type. Large fruits with a dark green and sometimes rough skin.

The name 'avocado' (not a*d*vocado) comes from the Spanish. The Spanish conquistadors who discovered the fruit called it *abogado,* a word probably derived from the Aztec name for the fruit, *ahuacatl,* meaning 'butter from the wood'. The avocado in modern Spanish is also called *aguacate.* The Aztec name is not only picturesque but also very descriptive. The creamy flesh of the avocado consists of only 70 per cent water, compared with 95-98 per cent in most other fruits. The rest consists mainly of unsaturated fatty acids, and because these are low in cholesterol the fruit is easy to digest.

Avocados are harvested unripe but post-ripen very well at room temperature. They post-ripen quicker wrapped in newspaper or in aluminium foil. The fruit is ripe when the skin yields to slight pressure. In fully ripe avocados the stone is loose — the fruit rattles when shaken. The riper the fruit, the fuller the taste.

Avocados should be cut and peeled immediately before use, because once cut the flesh quickly turns brown, although sprinkling with lemon juice or salt helps to prevent this. They should also be eaten raw — they taste unpleasantly bitter when cooked.

A fruit-laden avocado tree. Originally avocados came from Central and South America but now they have been introduced widely in Africa and the Mediterranean.

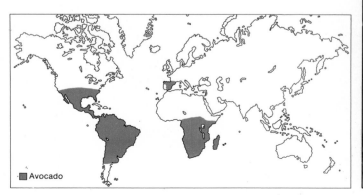

■ Avocado

△ Eduri, 5¼in (137mm) long

Avocado Pear
(Persea gratissima)

DESCRIPTION: Green, purple or almost black fruit with a smooth, rough or warty skin, 2-8in (5-20cm) long and round or pear-shaped. The flesh is greenish-white or yellow in colour, has a creamy texture and a slightly nutty taste. At the centre is a large stone that is easy to remove. Avocados can weigh from 3½-28oz (100-800g) depending on the variety.

COUNTRIES OF ORIGIN: Central and South America.

PRODUCER COUNTRIES: Israel, South and Central Africa, United States, Central and South America, Spain.

AVAILABILITY: All year from various producer countries.

USE: Cut the fruit in half lengthways down to the stone, carefully twist the two halves in opposite directions and the stone will come out. Halved pears can be scooped out and served as an appetizer with salt and pepper and lemon juice or vinaigrette. Alternatively, the flesh can be mixed with crab, prawns, finely chopped chicken, and other vegetables, or eaten as a dessert with sweetened cream. Avocado soup can be made from the puréed flesh mixed into warm stock (do not cook after adding avocados). Thin slices of avocado go well with ham in sandwiches, seasoned with salt, pepper, paprika powder, curry, tabasco, etc.

KEEPING QUALITIES: Once ripe, a few days in the salad drawer of the refrigerator.

NUTRITIONAL VALUE: 145-285 Kcal, 290 i.u. vitamin A, 5-30mg vitamin C, vitamin B, and lots of minerals per 100g serving.

INDUSTRIAL PROCESSING: None.

49

△ Hass, 3½in (9cm) long   ▽ Reid, 4in (10cm) long

Varieties

Bacon Variety grown in the United States, New Zealand and Spain, available from September to December. It is pear-shaped, with a green, warty skin and can be up to 6in (15cm) long. Looks like 'Fuerte'.

Eduri Quite a new variety, with a shiny, dark green skin and yellow to light green, very creamy flesh. Grown now in most producer countries and available from April to September.

Ettinger A very popular variety, like 'Fuerte', 'Hass' and 'Nabal'. The fruit is vivid green in colour with a dull, almost smooth skin. 'Ettingers' mainly come from Israel and South Africa and are available from September to December.

Fuerte An extremely important avocado variety, and also the most extensively grown, 'Fuerte' is pear-shaped, has a green lumpy skin and an excellent flavour; it can be 4-6in (10-15cm) long and weigh 7oz-1lb (200-450g). Imported throughout the year from Israel, Spain, South Africa.

△ Fuerte, 5in (122mm) long

Hass Of the 'alligator' type; has a very thick, warty, purplish-black skin. The flesh is creamy and deliciously nutty. Not only one of the most important but also one of the tastiest varieties. Mainly imported later in the year.

Nabal An almost spherical fruit with a fresh green, often slightly pimply skin. Imported from Israel from January to April. A fairly neutral taste, so suits both sweet and savoury dishes equally well.

Pollock Also called 'Pollack', an American variety grown mainly in Florida. It is a light green fruit with a smooth skin; it can grow up to 7in (18cm) long and weigh up to 1lb 9oz (700g). Exported between July and August.

Reid Mainly grown in Israel, with harvesting timed to extend avocado availability into June and July. Also grown extensively in New Zealand. It has a smooth, green skin and creamy-coloured flesh.

Waldin A large variety developed in Florida from a Guatemalan-type avocado and mainly grown in Florida, where harvesting takes place between August and the beginning of September. 'Waldin' is also cultivated in Mexico.

Leguminosae
Guama, carob, manna, tamarind

The *Leguminosae* or pulses form one of the largest plant groups on earth, in all comprising over 1,500 species, all of which bear seeds encased in long pods. These pods are the fruits. A pod is really a leaf that has grown together at the edges, forming a pocket inside which the seeds develop.

The pulses include some very important food crops, such as butter beans, French beans, broad beans, peas, chickpeas, haricot beans, red kidney beans, and so on, as well as fodder crops such as clover and lucerne. Some of these plants also make good rotation crops because they enrich the soil with nitrogen.

Nearly all the pulses are used as vegetables, but there are a few that, by taste and use, fall somewhere between a fruit and a vegetable. St. John's bread is a good example. This is the fruit of the carob tree, which grows around the Mediterranean; John the Baptist is supposed to have survived in the desert wilderness by eating carob pods, hence the name St. John's bread. The manna, from Southeast Asia, is also half way between a fruit and a vegetable. And so are the guama, from Central and South America, and the tamarind, which came originally from India but which is now grown in many tropical countries.

However, these fruits have not really caught on in the West and are usually only obtainable in specialist African or Indian shops. They are not exported in large quantities.

- ☐ Guama
- ☐ Carob
- ■ Manna, Tamarind

Guama
(Igna nobilis)
DESCRIPTION: Long, green and bumpy pods, 8-14in (20-35cm) long (the bumps are the seeds in the pod). The seeds contain a very sweet, dry pulp.
COUNTRIES OF ORIGIN: Central and South America.
PRODUCER COUNTRIES: Central and South America.
AVAILABILITY: May to January.
USE: Not known.
KEEPING QUALITIES: About a week.
NUTRITIONAL VALUE: Not known.
INDUSTRIAL PROCESSING: None.

Carob
(Ceratonia siliqua)
DESCRIPTION: Pods about 8in (20cm) long and 1¼in (3cm) wide containing 12 small, hard seeds. The pods are brownish-black and harden very quickly. Because the seeds always weigh the same, they were once used as standard measures for weighing gold and silver. The word 'carat' is derived from the Arabic *kirat*, meaning 'grain' or 'seed' which is in turn related to the Arabic word for the St. John's bread tree, *charrub*.
COUNTRY OF ORIGIN: Greece, Turkey.
PRODUCER COUNTRIES: Spain, Italy, Greece.
AVAILABILITY: July to February.
USE: The pods are usually chewed by children as candy. Chewing or grinding brings out the honey-sweet taste of the pod, which is why imitation chocolate is made from carob flour. Also used as a substitute for coffee as it contains no caffeine or oxalic acid.
KEEPING QUALITIES: A long time.
NUTRITIONAL VALUE: 30-50 per cent sugar.
INDUSTRIAL PROCESSING: Binding agent, imitation chocolate and coffee.

Manna
(Cassia fistula)
DESCRIPTION: Long, round, blackish brown pods, 12-20in (30-50cm) long. Pods contain numerous seeds in separate compartments, embedded in a sweet, blackish-brown pulp. The outside of the pod should not be eaten; only the seeds and the pulp are edible.
COUNTRIES OF ORIGIN: Southeast Asia.
PRODUCER COUNTRIES: Indonesia, India.
AVAILABILITY: June to October.
USE: The pulp is mainly used as a mild laxative.
KEEPING QUALITIES: A few weeks.
NUTRITIONAL VALUE: Not known.
INDUSTRIAL PROCESSING: The pharmaceutical industry uses the seeds to make a sweetener for diabetics; the tobacco industry uses the seeds to enhance the aroma of chewing tobacco.

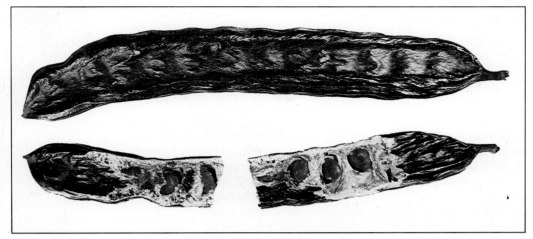

Tamarind
(Tamarindus indica)

DESCRIPTION: Rust-brown pods, 2-8in (5-20cm) long, easy to break open. Each pod contains up to ten compartments, each with a seed embedded in a dry, very sour pith. This pith contains as much as 16 per cent organic acids. Unripe pods are greenish-brown in colour.

COUNTRY OF ORIGIN: India.

PRODUCER COUNTRIES: India, Indonesia, some African countries.

AVAILABILITY: November to May.

USE: Both unripe and ripe pods are used in various Asiatic and African dishes. One use is tamarind water, made by finely grating the pith into lukewarm water. Tamarind syrup is also made, by removing the outer skin of the pod, soaking the pith and pips in water, pressing the mass through a sieve and then boiling with sugar. The syrup keeps for a long time in the refrigerator and makes a refreshing drink — add freshly-grated ginger, and top up with tap water. Or it can be used to make a sweet sauce — boil the diluted syrup, season with cinnamon, nutmeg and cardamom and thicken with cornflour.

KEEPING QUALITIES: A few weeks.

NUTRITIONAL VALUE: Vitamins A and C.

INDUSTRIAL PROCESSING: Syrup and dried pulp.

Meliaceae
Langsat

The *Meliaceae* family is related to the *Anacardiaceae*, the family to which the mango belongs. Opinions differ as to the number of species in this family of tropical trees and bushes; estimates range from 800 to 1500 species. Many are sources of valuable timber (including the wood once traditionally used for making cigar boxes). Others have shoots and fruits with an onion-like taste. In South America, parrots that eat these fruits are, in turn, eaten by the forest Indians who say the birds are very tasty because of their 'natural seasoning'. The 'puzzle fruit' comes from the Asiatic genus *Xylocarpus;* it contains approximately fifteen seeds of varying shape that fit neatly into one another and take hours to put back together once they have fallen out of the fruit.

As far as is known, only one member of the Meliaceae bears edible fruits: this is the tree known to botanists as *Lansium domesticum* (also called *L. parasiticum,* although there is nothing parasitic about it). *L.domesticum* grows to 80ft (25m) or more in height and occurs in Indonesia, Malaysia, Thailand and the Philippines, where the fruits are known by different names. Local nomenclature can be very confusing! In Java, for instance, the fruits are variously called langsat, duku, kokosan and lansep. Some people define langsat as the wild and duku as the cultivated form of the species, and the other two as naturally-occurring varieties. Even this is not a very clear distinction, because the fruits often differ from one another in colour, even if they come from the same variety. In their countries of origin these fruits are very popular, although they are not grown on a commercial basis. This is because no two trees produce identical fruits! Perhaps with careful selection and breeding the langsat will become more popular. Langsats are mainly imported into Europe and the United States for the benefit of the Asian population, and are difficult to find outside of specialized stores in big cities. There are no recipes for cooking langsats, even in their countries of origin; they are always eaten fresh.

Langsat
(Lansium domesticum)
DESCRIPTION: Yellowish- to brownish-yellow or greenish fruits, round or slightly oval in shape and 1-2in (2.5-5cm) long. The skin feels velvety to the touch because it is covered with short hairs. The juice is bitter and milky, and the slightly translucent white flesh sour and divided into four or five segments containing several fairly large, green, bitter pips.
COUNTRY OF ORIGIN: Malaysia.
PRODUCER COUNTRIES: Indonesia, Thailand, Philippines.
AVAILABILITY: March to June (irregular).
USE: Usually peeled and eaten fresh without the pips, but the sour flesh can be boiled, with a lot of sugar, to make syrup, jelly or jam.
KEEPING QUALITIES: A few days at room temperature; similar to mango.
NUTRITIONAL VALUE: Not known.
INDUSTRIAL PROCESSING: None.

△ A cluster of Langsats, individual fruits 1¾in (43mm) diameter

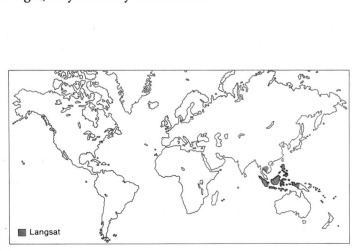

◼ Langsat

Moraceae
Breadfruit, jackfruit, red, white and black mulberry, marang, fig

The *Moraceae* family comprises around 1,000 species which differ from one another in the way they flower and in the shape of their fruits. But they all have one thing in common: their stems and leaves are full of milky sap. The family has three genera that produce well-known fruits: *Ficus,* which gives us figs; *Morus,* which gives us the white, the red and the black mulberry; and *Artocarpus,* which produces the breadfruit, the jackfruit and the marang.

The fig is a false fruit in that the pear-shaped body of the fruit is a receptacle that has grown around the real fruits; a fig is really a fleshy bag, with a small opening at the end, filled with a mass of fruits. On the walls of the bag grow hundreds of small flowerets that later change into the real fruits, the 'pips' of the fig. In the tropics, the flowers of the female trees are fertilized by pollen-carrying gall wasps which live in the male trees. They crawl through the tiny opening into the 'flower bag' and lay their eggs, at the same time transferring the pollen from the male trees onto the stigmas of the female flowers. There are also species of fig that bear unfertilized fruits without 'pips'. With cultivated figs, branches of wild, male trees, with their populations of gall wasps, are hung in the flowering female trees to ensure pollination. This is called *caprification.*

There are three kinds of mulberry: the American red mulberry, and the white and black mulberry which came originally from Asia. Mulberries look similar to blackberries, but the fleshy 'compartments' or fruitlets of a blackberry are juicy whereas the compartments of a mulberry are dry but surrounded by the fleshy, swollen parts of the flower. The mulberries introduced into Europe in the 17th and 18th centuries have now been supplanted by more modern varieties. The leaves are used as food for silkworms, though less so now since the advent of synthetic fibres.

The fruits of the genus *Artocarpus* are widely used in oriental cooking. The breadfruit (in some languages confused with the fruit of the baobab) is now grown in many tropical regions. When, in 1789, the notorious mutiny on the *Bounty* took place, the ship was actually on its way from the South Seas to the West Indies with breadfruit tree cuttings.

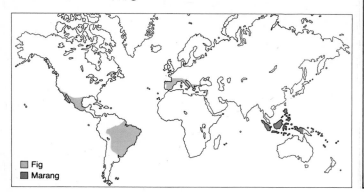

- Fig
- Marang

△ Jackfruit, 18in (460mm) long

Breadfruit
(Artocarpus communis)

DESCRIPTION: A large roundish fruit, 8-12in (20-30cm) long and 2-9lb (1-4kg) in weight, greenish brown in colour and covered with small, blunt spines. The unripe flesh has a slightly unpleasant smell but this fades as the fruit ripens. There are seeded and seedless varieties.

COUNTRIES OF ORIGIN: South Pacific region and Malaysia.

PRODUCER COUNTRIES: Indonesia, Thailand.

AVAILABILITY: Throughout the year.

USE: If ripe, peel and cut into slices; bake or cook unripe fruit. The seeds of the seed-bearing varieties can be roasted like chestnuts.

KEEPING QUALITIES: About two weeks at room temperature.

NUTRITIONAL VALUE: Not known.

INDUSTRIAL PROCESSING: None.

Jackfruit
(Artocarpus heterophylla)

DESCRIPTION: This is a very large, elongated fruit up to 3ft 3in (1m) long and up to 20in (0.5m) in diameter! The heaviest fruits can weigh up to 90lb (40kg) but exported specimens are generally smaller — 8-20in (20-50cm) long. The skin is yellowish-green in colour and covered with little knobbly scales. The white, cream or pink flesh is sweet and aromatic (jackfruits do not smell as unpleasant as breadfruits). The separate fruitlets inside the jackfruit contain flat, light brown seeds.

COUNTRIES OF ORIGIN: Southeast Asia.

PRODUCER COUNTRIES: Thailand, Indonesia, Kenya.

AVAILABILITY: Throughout the year.

USE: Peel, and eat the flesh raw, or bake or stew it. The seeds can be roasted and eaten in curries.

KEEPING QUALITIES: About two weeks at room temperature.

NUTRITIONAL VALUE: Not known.

INDUSTRIAL PROCESSING: None.

Marang
(Artocarpus champeden)

DESCRIPTION: In shape similar to the jackfruit, but smaller and darker in colour, especially the flesh. The flesh tastes extremely sweet and is very fragrant. The pips are round and dark brown.

COUNTRIES OF ORIGIN: India, Indonesia.

PRODUCER COUNTRIES: Indonesia, Philippines.

AVAILABILITY: December to February.

USE: As jackfruit.

KEEPING QUALITIES: As jackfruit.

NUTRITIONAL VALUE: Not known.

INDUSTRIAL PROCESSING: None.

White Mulberry
(Morus alba)

DESCRIPTION: Compound, bramble-like fruits ½-1½in (1-3cm) long, and creamish-white in colour. Quite a sweet taste.

COUNTRIES OF ORIGIN: Western Asia.

PRODUCER COUNTRIES: France, Italy, Chile, United States.

AVAILABILITY: June to August.

USE: Eat fresh or make into fruit salads or flan fillings. The leaves of the white mulberry are the staple diet of silkworms.

KEEPING QUALITIES: A few days.

NUTRITIONAL VALUE: High vitamin C content.

INDUSTRIAL PROCESSING: Jam or jelly.

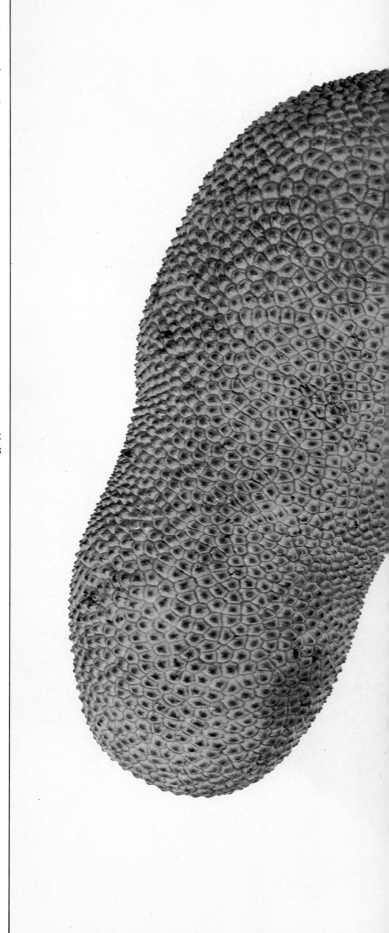

△ Marang, 12½in (322) long

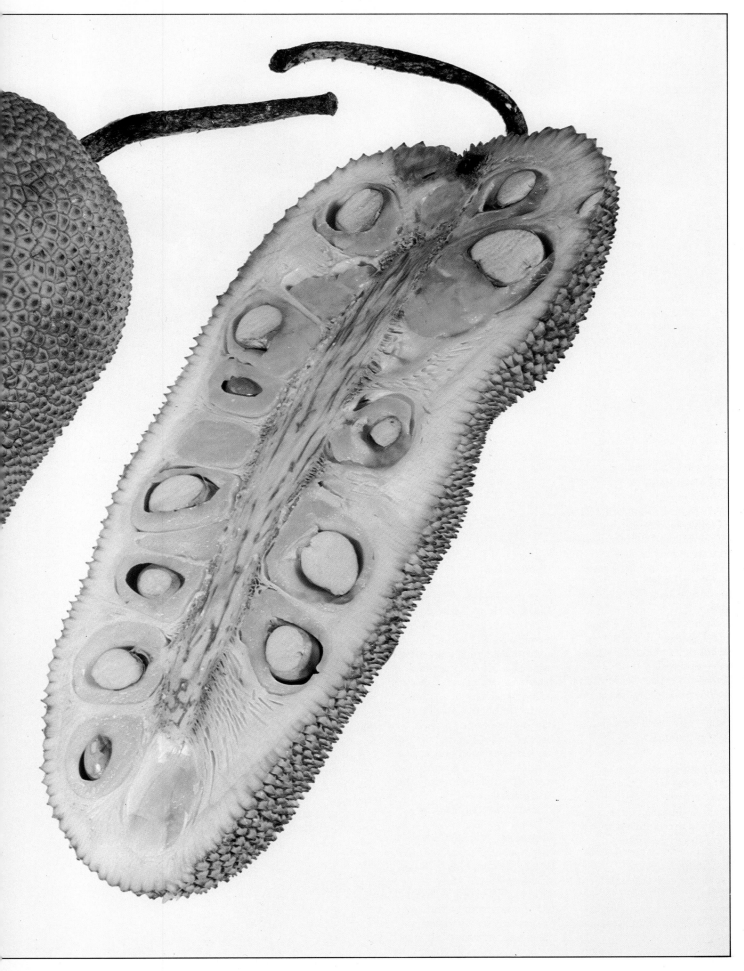

△ Black Mulberry, ¾in (19mm) long

Black Mulberry
(Morus nigra)
DESCRIPTION: Elongated, black, bramble-like fruits, a little larger than the white mulberry and tart-sweet in taste.

COUNTRIES OF ORIGIN: Persia, Southern Russia.

PRODUCER COUNTRIES: France, Italy.

AVAILABILITY: June to August.

USE: Eat fresh, or use in fruit salads or flan fillings, or make into jam or jelly.

KEEPING QUALITIES: A few days.

NUTRITIONAL VALUE: As white mulberry.

INDUSTRIAL PROCESSING: Jam, jelly and syrup.

Red Mulberry
(Morus rubra)
DESCRIPTION: Elongated, bramble-like fruits, varying in size, red in colour and with a refreshingly acid taste.

COUNTRIES OF ORIGIN: North and South America.

PRODUCER COUNTRIES: United States.

AVAILABILITY: July to August.

USE: Make into flan filling, jam or jelly.

KEEPING QUALITIES: Two days.

NUTRITIONAL VALUE: As white mulberry.

INDUSTRIAL PROCESSING: Jam and jelly.

Fig
(Ficus carica)
DESCRIPTION: A more or less pear-shaped, false fruit up to 3½in (8cm) long. Skin colour can vary from yellowish to deep purple with all kinds of intermediate hues, depending on the variety and ripeness. Inside, the fruit is whitish-pink or reddish in colour and may contain either masses of tiny edible pips or none at all, depending on whether the fruit has been fertilized or not. The taste can be sweet and aromatic but is often a little insipid. The skin is edible.

COUNTRIES OF ORIGIN: Asia Minor.

PRODUCER COUNTRIES: France, Italy, Greece, Spain, Israel, Brazil, Mexico, United States (California).

AVAILABILITY: April to January.

USE: Eat raw with or without skin, which is easy to peel, or cut in half and scoop out. Figs are best served chilled and taste good with raw ham or salami as an hors d'oeuvre, with cheese and French bread as a snack, sprinkled with kirsch liqueur or lemon juice and served with whipped cream as a dessert; as compote (simmer for five minutes in sugar and water, with vanilla pods, and leave to cool).

KEEPING QUALITIES: Ripe fruits: a few days. If brown or greyish spots appear on the skin, the fruit has turned sour and should not be eaten; these blemishes should not be confused with the natural 'bloom' on the skin, which can be wiped or washed off.

NUTRITIONAL VALUE: 205 Kcal, 2mg vitamin C, and traces of vitamins A and B per 100g serving.

INDUSTRIAL PROCESSING: Dried, canned, candied, syrup.

Varieties

Brown Turkey This variety, despite its name, is grown mainly in Israel, Italy and California and is available from April to January. The fruits are pear-shaped, 1½-2½in (4-6cm) long and have reddish-brown skin and purple flesh. They are sweet and juicy and are usually obtainable canned.

Celeste Comes mainly from Mexico and California and is available from November to January. The ripe fruits are purple, the pink flesh sweet and scented.

Kadota The most important fig variety from Italy, also known as 'Dotato' or 'Dottato'. A yellowish-green fig with purple flesh that may or may not contain seeds depending on the pollination method used during cultivation. Seedless fruits are 1½-2in (3-5cm) long, fruits with seeds are 2-3in (5-8cm) long. Fruits with seeds have a better, nuttier taste.

Sari Lob An important Mediterranean variety, mainly grown in France and Israel. The fruit is purplish-yellow and tends to burst open when ripe. It must then be eaten immediately. The taste is sweet and fragrant.

△ Celeste, 2in (49mm) diameter

△ Kadota, 3in (75mm) long   ▽ Sari Lob, 2in (49mm) diameter

Musaceae
Apple banana, plantain, dessert banana, pink
banana, rice banana

Botanists still disagree as to whether the banana (genus *Musa*) should be regarded as a separate family or whether it should belong, together with about five other genera, to the larger group *Musaceae*. The nomenclature of cultivated species of banana is confused. In everyday language, we simply distinguish between dessert bananas, which can be eaten raw, and cooking bananas, which have to be boiled, baked or prepared in some other way to make them palatable and digestible. Besides this distinction, we also give certain bananas specific common names, such as apple banana and rice banana. Some dessert bananas do, in fact, have variety names (e.g. Cavendish, Gros Michel) but they are seldom used because they tend to be sold under brand names such as Chiquita, Turbana, Fyffes, Geest, Dole and Del Monte. The varieties bought under such names, however, are all similar in taste and quality, although consumers usually learn by trial and error where to find bananas of the ripeness they prefer.

Bananas have been enjoyed for centuries and probably originated in Southeast Asia. From archaeological explorations there we know that they have been an important source of food for thousands of years.

Bananas grow in tropical and sub-tropical regions on large, bush-like plants. In commercially grown bananas, pollination is prevented and so no seeds form. The 'trunk' of a banana palm is really a compact mass of intertwined leaves. It shoots up from the roots of the plant and only bears fruit once. After that it dies, and the next crop grows on a new shoot or 'sucker' sent up from the roots.

The bananas themselves grow on stems that emerge from the trunk. Each stem sprouts ten or more overlapping 'hands', with 12-16 'fingers' or bananas in each hand. A single stem can carry 120-200 bananas. Bananas are harvested by cutting off the whole stem with all its hands. Before shipment, the 'hands' are detached from the stem and packed in boxes.

Bananas are harvested unripe, because ripe ones tend to burst open and become floury and lose their taste. They post-ripen exceptionally well, better than any other fruit, although they still need careful handling to keep them in good condition ready for sale. With the advent of rapid transport and modern refrigeration techniques, bananas have become popular all over the world. On modern banana plantations, the fruits are harvested when they are still grass-green. They are despatched to their destination countries very quickly in refrigerated containers. They are then stored for four to ten days in special ripening warehouses where temperature, ventilation and humidity are precision-controlled. When they have turned yellow, they are sent out to the retailers. Ethylene gas is used to help them turn yellow.

However, only dessert bananas are post-ripened in this way. The more robust plantains or cooking varieties are handled less meticulously, which is why they often look a little the worse for wear.

Bananas are grown in all tropical countries, but most imports come from South and Central American countries, the so-called banana republics, and to a lesser extent from Africa. Only a few special varieties, such as the rice banana and the apple banana, come from Southeast Asia.

*Banana harvest in Surinam; the plastic
wrapping is a protection against birds.*

Dessert Banana
Apple Banana,   Pink Banana, Rice Banana

Apple Banana
(Musa sp.)

DESCRIPTION: Small, stocky banana, 3-4in (8-10cm) long, usually on sale in hands or half hands. The very thin, smooth skin quickly changes from green to golden-yellow. The flesh tastes pleasantly sweet and has a hint of apple.

COUNTRIES OF ORIGIN: Southeast Asia.

PRODUCER COUNTRIES: Thailand, Indonesia, Ivory Coast.

AVAILABILITY: Throughout the year.

USE: As dessert banana.

KEEPING QUALITIES: About one week at room temperature, depending on ripeness.

NUTRITIONAL VALUE: More or less as dessert banana.

INDUSTRIAL PROCESSING: None.

△ Apple Banana, 4in (10cm) long　▽ Valery, 5½in (14cm) long

63

△ Plantain, 9in (23cm) long

Plantain
(Musa sp.)

DESCRIPTION: Green or greenish-yellow cooking banana, generally with a lot of brown scars or spots; 12-15in (30-40cm) long and less curved than many dessert bananas. Plantains can usually be bought individually, rather than in hands. The hard skin is much more difficult to remove than that of the dessert banana. The flesh is very floury and cannot be eaten raw.

COUNTRIES OF ORIGIN: Southeast Asia.

PRODUCER COUNTRIES: Colombia, Panama, Brazil, tropical Africa.

AVAILABILITY: Throughout the year.

USE: Remove the skin by cutting the ends off the fruit, then cutting the skin lengthwise a few times and stripping it off. Slice the flesh into rings or strips and boil, bake or grill.

KEEPING QUALITIES: About one week at room temperature.

NUTRITIONAL VALUE: 158 Kcal per 100g serving, but virtually no vitamins.

INDUSTRIAL PROCESSING: Dried.

Dessert Banana
(Musa paradisiaca)

DESCRIPTION: Yellow or yellowish-green, usually rather curved fruits, often sold in 'hands'. Length can vary from 6-12in (15-30cm). The whitish-yellow flesh has a bland, slightly rough taste, which gets sweeter as the fruit ripens. Bananas are not fully ripe until the skin starts to turn brown.

COUNTRIES OF ORIGIN: Southeast Asia.

PRODUCER COUNTRIES: Panama, Costa Rica, Honduras, Guatemala, Colombia, Ecuador, Brazil, Somalia, Ivory Coast, Nigeria, Cameroon.

AVAILABILITY: Throughout the year.

USE: Remove skin and eat flesh raw, or use in fruit salads, cakes, milkshakes, etc.

KEEPING QUALITIES: Four to five days at room temperature; longer in the refrigerator.

NUTRITIONAL VALUE: 90 Kcal, 430 i.u. vitamin A, 10mg vitamin C, and traces of vitamins B1, B2 and B6 per 100g serving.

INDUSTRIAL PROCESSING: Dried, pulp.

Varieties

Cavendish *(Musa cavendishii)* An extremely popular dessert banana, grown extensively in all producer countries. There is also a 'Giant Cavendish' variety. 'Cavendish' came originally from China and has overtaken 'Gros Michel' in popularity because it is more resistant to wind damage, as well as to Panama disease, to which bananas are particularly susceptible.

Gros Michel or **Big Mike** One of the first varieties to be grown for export, because it handles and stores easily. It is also called the West Indian or Jamaican banana and has been known in Central America since 1836. Varieties similar to 'Gros Michel' are grown on Martinique and Guadeloupe under the names 'Makandia' and 'Raimbaud'. 'Big Mike' is still grown commercially in Colombia and Ecuador, but has been overtaken on the market by 'Cavendish'.

△ Gros Michel, 6in (17cm) long

Lacatan A natural mutant of 'Cavendish'. The major producer countries are Brazil and Cameroon.

Robusta Also called 'Poyo', this variety was developed from 'Cavendish', and is shorter and stockier. The taste is also sweeter. Mainly exported from the Ivory Coast.

Valery This variety was developed by the United Fruit Company from Asiatic stock as a quality banana designed specifically to fulfil market needs. It dates from the 1920s and the name is now a registered trade mark. The taste is sweet and fragrant and remarkably consistent (see picture on page 63).

△ Pink Banana, 6¼ in (156mm) long

Pink Banana
(Musa sp.)
DESCRIPTION: The various varieties in this group are distinguished by their greenish-red to reddish colour and their pink flesh.
COUNTRIES OF ORIGIN: Southeast Asia.
PRODUCER COUNTRIES: Ivory Coast, Thailand, Indonesia.
AVAILABILITY: Throughout the year.

USE: Some varieties can be eaten as dessert bananas; others should be cooked like plantains.
KEEPING QUALITIES: As plantain.
NUTRITIONAL VALUE: Not known.
INDUSTRIAL PROCESSING: None.

△ Rice Banana, 4½in (115mm) long

Rice Banana
(Musa sp.)
DESCRIPTION: Small unribbed
banana, 1½-3in (6-8cm) long,
yellow in colour, with very
sweet and easily digestible
flesh.
COUNTRIES OF ORIGIN: Southeast
Asia.
PRODUCER COUNTRIES:
Indonesia, Thailand.
AVAILABILITY: Throughout the
year.

USE: Peel and eat raw or baked.
KEEPING QUALITIES: A few days
at room temperature.
NUTRITIONAL VALUE: Not
known.
INDUSTRIAL PROCESSING: None.

Myrtaceae
Feijoa, Brazilian cherry, guava, water rose, rose apple

The large myrtle or *Myrtaceae* family has approximately 80 genera and 3,000 species but produces only a few edible fruits, of which only one, the guava, has become commercially popular. All the others, used only in oriental or South American cooking, are exported irregularly and in very limited quantities.

But some members of this family give us other interesting products. For example, cloves are the dried flower buds of *Syzygium aromaticum*. They have played an important role in world affairs, because it was partly to exploit this spice that enterprising Europeans travelled the high seas and set up trading colonies. Another important genus is *Eucalyptus*, various species of which produce fragrant oils, commercially valuable gums, or durable timber. The leaves of *Melaleuca leucadendra* yield cajaput oil, a very effective remedy for muscular pain, headache, toothache and minor wounds.

Myrtus communis, from the Mediterranean, is well known for quite a different reason: it is the myrtle of Greek and Roman mythology, and was considered sacred to Aphrodite (Venus), the goddess of love. Even today, virgin brides in some Southern European countries carry a myrtle bouquet on their wedding day.

The edible fruits of the *Myrtaceae* family originally came from the Americas and to a lesser extent from the Far East. But they have since prospered in other tropical and sub-tropical areas. Cuttings crossed continents very early on and more varieties were introduced into Southeast Asia than left it. But none of these varieties has yet succeeded in breaking into the American or European market, partly because their taste does not suit the Western palate, but also because they do not keep well and are difficult to transport.

△ Water Rose, 2¾in (68mm) diameter

Feijoa
(Feijoa sellowiana)
DESCRIPTION: A round or oval fruit, 1½-4in (3-10cm) long and ¾-2in (2-5cm) in diameter. The skin is green and shiny. The flesh is firm and tastes a bit like pineapple. The seeds sit in a core divided into five compartments.

COUNTRY OF ORIGIN: Brazil.

PRODUCER COUNTRIES: Brazil, New Zealand, southern United States.

AVAILABILITY: Throughout the year.

USE: Halve the fruit, scoop out flesh and eat raw. Can also be used in fruit salads, jam and compote.

KEEPING QUALITIES: Two or three days at room temperature; about one week in the refrigerator.

NUTRITIONAL VALUE: 40-100g vitamin C per 100g serving.

INDUSTRIAL PROCESSING: None.

Brazilian Cherry
(Eugenia uniflora)
DESCRIPTION: Ovoid, eight-ribbed fruits, ¾-2in (3-5cm) long, varying in colour from light red to deep black. The lighter the colour, the sweeter the fruit. The skin is thin and the flesh is soft and juicy, with one spherical or two hemispherical pips.

COUNTRY OF ORIGIN: Brazil.

PRODUCER COUNTRIES: Brazil, Surinam, Indonesia, Thailand.

AVAILABILITY: Throughout the year from various producer countries.

USE: Eat fresh, including the skin; use in fruit salads etc., or make into jam.

KEEPING QUALITIES: One or two days at room temperature.

NUTRITIONAL VALUE: Not known.

INDUSTRIAL PROCESSING: Fruit syrup.

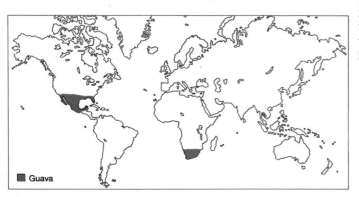

■ Guava

△ Guava, 3½in (88mm) diameter

Guava
(Psidium guajava)
DESCRIPTION: Pear-shaped fruit, up to 4½in (12cm) long and usually with a green or yellow skin. Ripe fruits give off a wonderful fragrance and feel slightly squashy. The flesh is greenish-white, pink or dark red, depending on the variety, and contains a lot of edible pips arranged in a ring. The flesh tastes sweet-tart and has a very distinctive aroma.

COUNTRIES OF ORIGIN: Tropical America.

PRODUCER COUNTRIES: South Africa, Thailand, southern United States, Mexico.

AVAILABILITY: Throughout the year from various producer countries.

USE: Peel like an ápple, cut into four, remove pips if desired and eat on its own, or use in desserts and fruit salad. The flesh can also be made into purée (press through a sieve to remove the pips), and used in ice-cream or yoghurt or as a cake filling.

KEEPING QUALITIES: About one week at room temperature; longer in the refrigerator. Do not keep below 46°F (8°C).

NUTRITIONAL VALUE: 70 Kcal, 200-1100 i.u. vitamin A, and 200-1000mg vitamin C per 100g serving.

INDUSTRIAL PROCESSING: Canned in syrup, juice, jelly, compote and purée.

Water Rose
(Syzygium aquea)
DESCRIPTION: Bright red fruit, shaped like a top, ¾-1in (2-3cm) long and 1½-2in (4-5cm) across. The sweet and very aromatic flesh is white, pink or blood-red in colour and contains one or more small pips; it is juicy and thirst-quenching. Because of its thin skin and high moisture content the fruit goes off quickly.

COUNTRIES OF ORIGIN: Southeast Asia.

PRODUCER COUNTRIES: Thailand, Malaysia, Indonesia.

AVAILABILITY: June to September.

USE: Eat on its own or use in fruit salads, etc.

KEEPING QUALITIES: Very short.

NUTRITONAL VALUE: High in vitamin A and sugar.

INDUSTRIAL PROCESSING: Fruit syrup.

Rose Apple
(Syzygium jambus)
DESCRIPTION: Similar in shape to the water rose but with the calyx more closed up. The skin is yellowish-green with pinkish-red streaks. The flesh is dry and smells of roses.

COUNTRY OF ORIGIN: Malaysia.

PRODUCER COUNTRIES: Thailand, Indonesia.

AVAILABILITY: November to April.

USE: Eat fresh on its own or use less juicy fruits in jam or marmalade.

KEEPING QUALITIES: Three to four days at room temperature.

NUTRITIONAL VALUE: Not known.

INDUSTRIAL PROCESSING: Fruit syrup.

Oxalidaceae
Cucumber tree fruit, star apple

The 800 or so species of the *Oxalidaceae* or wood sorrel family grow mainly in the tropics and sub-tropics. A few species also grow in more temperate climates, spreading into northern parts of Europe, Asia and America. Only one genus, *Averrhoa*, produces edible fruits, in the form of cucumber tree fruits and star apples. These are very closely related and are mainly used in oriental cooking. They can often be found in the West in shops serving local Asian communities. The close relationship between these two fruits is reflected in their Malay names: *blimbing asem* (cucumber tree fruit) and *blimbing manis — asem* means sour, and *manis* means sweet. As the names suggest, the two fruits differ in taste, but they also differ in size, the star apple being the larger.

Both fruits grow on relatively small trees with lots of branches and attractive, feathered leaves. The genus they belong to, *Averrhoa*, is named after the Moorish philosopher, physician and astronomer Averroes (Abu al-Walid Muhammad ibn Ahmed ibn Muhammad ibn Rushd), who lived in the 12th century in Cordoba in Spain and who was probably the first to describe the genus. In the 17th century the star apple was also sketched and described by Georg Rumpf, a German-born official in the service of the Dutch East India Company and author of *The Amboina Herb Book*.

△ Cucumber Tree Fruit, 2½in (68mm) long

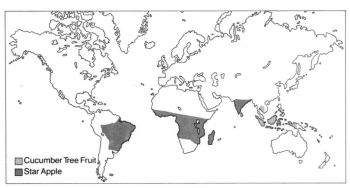

☐ Cucumber Tree Fruit
■ Star Apple

Cucumber Tree Fruit
(Averrhoa bilimbi)
DESCRIPTION: A greenish-yellow, translucent fruit, 3in (8cm) long, with a sour taste and a five-pointed star shape in cross-section. Ripe fruits also smell sour.
COUNTRY OF ORIGIN: Malaysia.
PRODUCER COUNTRIES: Thailand, Indonesia, Sri Lanka.
AVAILABILITY: As star apple (q.v.).
USE: Not suitable for eating raw. Usually made into compote (simmered with sugar), preserved in salt, vinegar or sugar syrup, or used as a chutney ingredient.
KEEPING QUALITIES: As star apple.
NUTRITIONAL VALUE: As star apple.
INDUSTRIAL PROCESSING: Syrup, chutneys.

△ Star Apple, 5in (122mm) long

Star Apple
(Averrhoa carambola)

DESCRIPTION: A five-pointed star in cross-section, about 4in (12cm) long, with brilliant yellow, translucent skin. The flesh is slightly sweet and crunchy and has an aftertaste rather like fresh green peas. The large varieties are the sweetest and most delicious.

COUNTRIES OF ORIGIN: India, Sri Lanka.

PRODUCER COUNTRIES: Thailand, Sri Lanka, India, tropical Africa, Brazil, Israel.

AVAILABILITY: July to September, and December to April, from various producer countries.

USE: The sweeter varieties can be eaten raw. The skin is rather difficult to digest, so the flesh is usually scraped out. Unripe, smaller, less sweet fruits can be made into compote (simmered with sugar), or used in sweet and sour dishes, or mixed with other fruit in flans.

KEEPING QUALITIES: About a week at room temperature; longer in the refrigerator. Do not keep below 41°F (5°C).

NUTRITIONAL VALUE: High in vitamin C.

INDUSTRIAL PROCESSING: Canned in syrup, juice, jam and jelly.

Palmae
Awarra, corozo, date, coconut, salak

The tropical *Palmae* (or *Palmaceae)* family comprises around 4,000 species, most of which are only now being studied by horticulturists. Many of them are tall trees with a crown of fan-shaped leaves. Others do not grow as tall and some are even climbing plants. The family as a whole is of great commercial value, providing such products as sago, raffia, rattan, copra and many vegetable oils and fats. In the tropics, all kinds of palm trees are used as building materials or made into furniture or tools and other implements. The best known palm fruits, of course, are the date and the coconut.

We do not know where the date palm originally came from. It was cultivated in the Middle East as early as 3000 BC, and now grows in many other countries — it was introduced into California and Arizona, for example. The dried fruits have always been an important source of food for the peoples of North Africa and the Near East. Dried dates keep for a very long time, are nutritious and can easily be carried around by nomadic tribes, who call them 'bread of the desert'. The date palm is dioecious — trees are either male or female. The female trees can grow up to 80ft (25m). The fruits develop on stalks in the axil or junction point between leaf and stem, high above the ground. As many as 40 clusters, each carrying 25-30 dates, can grow from a single axil, and up to 330lb (50kg) dates can be picked from a prolific palm. Harvesting is from mid-September to the end of November. Date palms are firmly associated in most people's minds with desert or semi-desert climates, but they like to have moisture at their roots, which makes them typical oasis and coastal palms.

Until very recently only dried dates or semi-dried dates appeared on the international market. Dried dates, usually pressed into blocks, are quite hard and a bit tasteless; semi-dried dates, usually arranged on plastic stalks in narrow oval boxes, are sweeter and juicier, and generally very sticky.

For a few years now, however, fresh or rather fresh-frozen dates have been appearing in the shops, mainly produced in California and Israel. The fruits are deep-frozen to a temperature of -13°F (-25°C) immediately after harvesting. Because they contain very little water and a lot of sugar and because no preservatives are added to enhance the taste, deep-freezing has no detrimental effect. If deep-frozen dates are defrosted shortly before sale, they are virtually as fresh as the day they were picked. Fresh-frozen dates are more flavoursome, less sweet and much less sticky than semi-dried ones. They should be eaten within about five days of defrosting; they should not be refrozen.

The coconut has also been cultivated for a very long time. Coconut palms grow in nearly all tropical regions today and often reach a height of 100ft (30m). The fruits develop between the vertical leaves at the crown of the palm. Many parts of the coconut palm are extremely useful: the dried pulp of the coconuts themselves gives us copra from which oil is pressed for making soap and margarine; the hearts of the young shoots are eaten as a vegetable, and sometimes canned; for centuries, mats and even hut walls and roofs have been woven from the leaves and leaf fibres; and the wood and nut shells have been used for making furniture, tools, flooring products, building timber and so on.

A young coconut is almost all milk inside, with only a slippery coating of white flesh adhering to the shell. The milk is very nutritious, as well as delicious, and is often used to marinade meat for curries. At this stage the flesh can be scooped away from the shell with a spoon. As the coconut matures, the flesh thickens and hardens, absorbing the milk. In this form coconut is far less digestible.

One up-and-coming palm tree fruit is the salak, an unusual looking pear-shaped fruit with a skin like an armadillo's. The salak comes from Southeast Asia and grows on a palm that has virtually no trunk. It is difficult to harvest because the leaves of the palm are covered with large sharp spines. Like two other palm fruits, the awarra and the corozo, the salak is exported only occasionally and only to satisfy the demands of local Asian communities.

Date palms giving shade in an oasis in Iraq.

- Coconut
- Date

Awarra
(Astrocaryum vulgare)
DESCRIPTION: A more or less round fruit, 1-2½in (2-6cm) long, with a dirty brown or dirty orange skin. Contains almost no flesh between the skin and large hard pit.
COUNTRY OF ORIGIN: South America.
PRODUCER COUNTRIES: Most South American countries.
AVAILABILITY: November to June.
USE: In local cooking, the skin is used for colouring rice yellow.
KEEPING QUALITIES: A few weeks.

Corozo
(Bactris minor)
DESCRIPTION: A round fruit, 1¼- 4in (3-10cm) across. As it ripens, it changes from bleached white to brownish-yellow, red, or even violet, depending on the variety. Several close relatives of the corozo have the same name, which causes great confusion.
COUNTRIES OF ORIGIN: From Panama to Colombia.
PRODUCER COUNTRIES: Brazil, Colombia, Peru.
AVAILABILITY: January to May (sporadically).
USE: After peeling, eat fresh without the pip(s); use the rather sour juice fresh or make into jelly with gelatine.

Date
(Phoenix dactylifera)
DESCRIPTION: About 2in (5cm) long and ½in (1cm) across. The skin is shiny brown to honey-coloured, sometimes even red. The single, very hard pit is long and round in cross-section. The flesh tastes of honey, but is not excessively sweet when the fruit is fresh.
COUNTRIES OF ORIGIN: Middle East.
PRODUCER COUNTRIES: Fresh-frozen dates: California, Israel. Dried and semi-dried or jam-making quality: Iraq, Saudi Arabia, Iran, Tunisia, Algeria, Spain, California.
AVAILABILITY: Throughout the year.
USE: To remove the skin, if desired, cut off the end and squeeze the flesh out, or cut the date in half lengthways, take out the pit and press the flesh out of the skin. Eat on its own

△ Awarra, 1½in (35mm) across

or with cheese or wrapped in bacon. Combines well in fruit salads with apple, pear, orange, raisins, and cinnamon.
KEEPING QUALITIES: Fresh-frozen dates after defrosting: two days at room temperature, five days in the refrigerator. In the deep freeze: for several months provided they have not already been defrosted. Dried dates: several months.
NUTRITIONAL VALUE: Fresh fruits: very variable. Dried fruits are 60-70 per cent sugar, and contain 275 Kcal, 50 i.u. vitamin A, and traces of vitamin B per 100g serving.

INDUSTRIAL PROCESSING: Dried, semi-dried, deep-frozen, jam, purée.

73

Varieties

Deglet Nour Also called 'Deglet Noor' or 'Deglet Ennour' or 'Muscat', the world's most widely commercially grown variety. Fresh-frozen dates are mainly of this variety, although 'Khadrawi' and 'Hallawi' can also be frozen. Tunisia, Algeria and the United States export 'Deglet Nour' dried and semi-dried. Golden-yellow and slightly transparent, with pit visible from the outside.

Hallawi The best date variety grown in Iraq. Light brown, up to 2in (5cm) long. Exported fresh-frozen and dried from Israel and dried only from Iraq.

Khadrawi Called 'Chadrawi' in Israel and very similar to 'Hallawi' in size and appearance, though the flesh tends to be drier.

Siar or **Sayer** Usually a drying variety, and mainly exported by Israel and Tunisia. Because 'Siar' is a very dry date, it is used a great deal for making date bread (*tamar* or *tammer*).

△ Salak, 2in (5cm) across

Salak
(Zalacca edulis)

DESCRIPTION: Round in shape, and 1-2½in (3-6cm) long. The skin is shiny, reddish-brown, made up of hard, overlapping scales closing to a point at the end of the fruit. There are both red and white varieties. The yellowish-white flesh consists of three sections enclosed in a transparent membrane. Each section contains a round or oval, brown, inedible pit. Ripe fruits are sweet-tart in taste; unripe fruits give off an unpleasant smell.

COUNTRIES OF ORIGIN: Southeast Asia.

PRODUCER COUNTRIES: Thailand, Indonesia.

AVAILABILITY: February to April.

USE: Peel back skin of ripe fruits, starting near the point, or remove skin by rubbing against the lie of the scales. Take the three flesh sections out and rub away the enclosing membranes. Eat on its own or use in fruit salads or desserts. Peel unripe fruits in the same way and simmer in water with sugar until soft. Cool and serve. Unripe fruits can also be made into a tasty side dish by cutting off the pointed end and soaking them for a minimum of four days in a bowl of water in which four tablespoons of salt and four tablespoons of sugar have been dissolved.

KEEPING QUALITIES: A few days in the refrigerator.

NUTRITIONAL VALUE: Not known.

INDUSTRIAL PROCESSING: Canned.

Coconut
(Cocos nucifera)

DESCRIPTION: Elongated or round fruit, 4-6in (10-15cm) long and covered all over with brown fibres that are the middle layer of the fruit wall, (the outer layer sloughs off as the fruit ripens and the innermost layer is the 'shell' of the coconut). The three dark indentations on the stalk end are left by the leaves from which the ovary was formed. Two of them are only shallow dents; the third, in fact, has an opening through which the germinating seed finds its way to the outside to put down roots. The shell contains white, oily and fibrous flesh; in unripe coconuts the flesh is a milky white liquid.

COUNTRIES OF ORIGIN: Asia.

PRODUCER COUNTRIES: Nearly all tropical countries.

AVAILABILITY: Throughout the year from various producer countries.

USE: Drill two holes into the shell, and drink the coconut milk (even better chilled). Crack the shell open with a hammer, score the flesh and dig out with a stout knife. Eat the flesh on its own or grate and use in cakes, ice-cream, curries, confectionery, etc.

KEEPING QUALITIES: A long time if left whole, but the milk dries out if left too long (shake the coconut to see if milk is still there).

NUTRITIONAL VALUE: High calorie content because of the high oil content.

INDUSTRIAL PROCESSING: Canned coconut milk; dried; processed to obtain edible oil and raw material for soap and margarine manufacture.

◁ Coconut, 5in (127mm) diameter   ▽ Siar, 1¾in (45mm) diameter

Passifloraceae
Passionfruit, sweet granadilla, banana passionfruit, giant granadilla

Most members of the *Passifloraceae* family belong to the genus *Passiflora*, the passion flower. Over 400 species, mainly American, take their generic name from the characteristic shape of the flowers — in many countries the parts of the flower (stigmas, stamens, crown leaves and sepals) are seen as symbolizing the instruments of torture associated with Christ's Passion. When Spanish missionaries first saw the flowers in the jungles of South America, so the story goes, they interpreted them as divine inspiration to convert the Indians to Christianity as quickly as possible, if necessary by force. And that is exactly what happened.

Only a few *Passiflora* species have edible fruits and of these only a few have reached world markets. The best known of these are the purple and yellow passionfruit. Less frequently seen in the shops are the giant granadilla and the banana passionfruit. At present in New Zealand there are intensive efforts being made to develop a commercially viable banana passionfruit. As the name 'granadilla' suggests, the fruit has a Spanish heritage; it reminded the Spanish conquistadors of the pomegranate, and so they called it *granadilla,* meaning 'little pomegranate'.

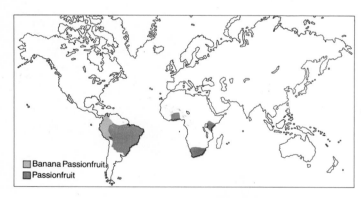

Banana Passionfruit / Passionfruit

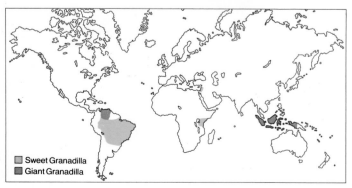

Sweet Granadilla / Giant Granadilla

Passionfruit
(Passiflora edulis)
DESCRIPTION: A round, sometimes slightly ovoid fruit, 2-3in (5-8cm) long and deep purple in colour. The thin, tough skin is smooth but wrinkles very quickly as the fruit loses moisture, though this does not affect the eating quality or the characteristic aroma. The juicy, greenish flesh contains soft, edible pips. The taste is tart but sweet, and the smell very fragrant.
COUNTRY OF ORIGIN: Brazil.
PRODUCER COUNTRIES: Kenya, Ivory Coast, South Africa, Brazil.
AVAILABILITY: Throughout the year from various producer countries.
USE: Halve the fruits and scoop out the flesh and pips. Eat chilled and sprinkled with lemon juice. Mix with whipped or sour cream, use in fruit salads, or add to juices or jams.
KEEPING QUALITIES: A few days at room temperature; longer in the refrigerator. Use up wrinkled fruits quickly, otherwise they dry out.
NUTRITIONAL VALUE: 75 Kcal, 700 i.u. vitamin A, 20mg vitamin C, and 1.5 mg vitamin B12 per 100g serving.
INDUSTRIAL PROCESSING: Mainly juice.

Sweet Granadilla
(Passiflora edulis var. flavicarpa)
DESCRIPTION: Yellow or orange fruits, 2-3in (5-8cm) in diameter, with a thick, hard skin that protects them very efficiently against drying out. Sweet granadillas usually stay more attractive to look at than passionfruit, but are often less tasty.

COUNTRY OF ORIGIN: Brazil.
PRODUCER COUNTRIES: Kenya, Israel, Brazil.
AVAILABILITY: Throughout the year.
USE: As passionfruit.
KEEPING QUALITIES: As passionfruit.
NUTRITIONAL VALUE: As passionfruit.
INDUSTRIAL PROCESSING: Juice.

Banana Passionfruit
(Passiflora mollissima)
DESCRIPTION: Oval fruits, 3-4½in (8-12cm) long, yellow in colour and with a fairly hard skin. The flesh tastes deliciously sweet.
COUNTRIES OF ORIGIN: South America.
PRODUCER COUNTRIES: Peru, Venezuela, Colombia.
AVAILABILITY: Throughout the year.
USE: Halve and scoop out flesh. Eat fresh.
KEEPING QUALITIES: Ten days at room temperature.
NUTRITIONAL VALUE: Not known.
INDUSTRIAL PROCESSING: None.

△ Passionfruit, 2in (50mm) across   ▽ Sweet Granadilla, 2½in (55mm) across

Giant Granadilla
(Passiflora quadrangularis)
DESCRIPTION: Yellow or
yellowish-green fruit, usually
with purple spots, and 8-12in
(20-30cm) in diameter. The
skin is ¾-1½in (2-3cm) thick. The
flesh tastes quite acidic and is
mainly used for making juice.
COUNTRIES OF ORIGIN: South
America.
PRODUCER COUNTRIES: Brazil,
Venezuela, Indonesia.
AVAILABILITY: Throughout the
year.
USE: Halve and scoop out the
flesh; eat on its own or make
into juice.
KEEPING QUALITIES: Ten days at
room temperature.
NUTRITIONAL VALUE: Not
known.
INDUSTRIAL PROCESSING: Juice,
liqueur (maracuja liqueur).

Punicaceae
Pomegranate

The *Punicaceae* family consists of just one species with two varieties: the common pomegranate *(Punica granatum)* and a very rare species only found on the small island of Socotra in the Indian Ocean.

The pomegranate, from which we get grenadine syrup, originally came from Persia, but it has been cultivated in sub-tropical parts of Europe, Asia and North Africa for thousands of years. With the grape and the fig, it plays a part in the mythology and traditions of the Middle East, where all three fruits are symbols of fertility, wealth and prosperity.

Pomegranates grow on bushes or trees that can reach a height of 26ft (8m). The thick, leathery skin keeps the fruit juicy for a very long time, as much an advantage to the ancient desert traveller as it is to fruit export and import companies today.

Today pomegranates are cultivated in most countries with a sub-tropical climate, including North America. There is a romantic belief that the nearer to Persia they grow, the more perfumed they are. However, all pomegranates, wherever they are grown, have one thing in common, and that is their large number of edible seeds. The seeds of the wild pomegranate, according to one old wive's tale, number 613, as many as there are laws in the Bible. No one knows if this is true or not. There are several cultivated varieties (e.g. Spanish Ruby, Tendral) but they are seldom referred to by name.

The juice and broken skin of a pomegranate produce stains that are almost impossible to remove, hence the pomegranate's long history as a dye source, for Persian rugs, for example. Some varieties are grown as ornamental shrubs because of their very attractive red (sometimes white) flowers.

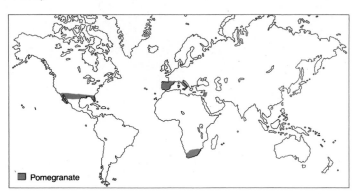

Pomegranate

△ Pomegranate, 4in (96mm) diameter

Pomegranate
(Punica granatum)
DESCRIPTION: A round, sometimes slightly egg-shaped fruit, 3-4in (8-12cm) in diameter, with a leathery, yellowish-red skin up to ½-1in (1-3cm) thick that turns brown if the fruit is kept for a long time. Inside, the fruit is sub-divided by whitish membranes into six compartments. In each of these there are countless edible pips embedded in juicy, light to dark red flesh. Beware! the juice from the skin and flesh causes stains that are almost impossible to remove.
COUNTRY OF ORIGIN: Iran (Persia).
PRODUCER COUNTRIES: Spain, Italy, Israel, South Africa, United States.
AVAILABILITY: July to March.
USE: Slit the skin several times from the calyx to the base of the stalk (as with an orange). To remove the pips and flesh, hold the fruit calyx down, over a plate and peel the skin back. Ripe fruits can also be cut in half, placed cut side down on a plate and tapped with a knife to loosen the pips and the flesh. Or you can cut the fruit in half and spoon out the flesh and pips. Do not eat the white membranes. Or squeeze the flesh out into a sieve and strain off the juice to make a refreshing chilled drink.
KEEPING QUALITIES: Fruits keep for a long time because of their very thick skin.
NUTRITIONAL VALUE: 77Kcal and 5mg vitamin C per 100g serving.
INDUSTRIAL PROCESSING: Juice, grenadine syrup.

Rhamnaceae
Jujube

The small *Rhamnaceae* family has only one genus that produces edible fruit, *Ziziphus*, of which only the yellow, date-shaped fruits of *Ziziphus jujuba*, called jujubes, jujulas or even Chinese dates, are occasionally on sale in the West.

This small genus is believed to have come originally from India, but it spread from there to China, where one of its species produces fruits as large as hen's eggs. The jujubes imported into America and Europe, however, are much smaller and come mainly from Thailand. The yellowish-brown jujubes sold in France and Italy are grown around the Mediterranean, and are the fruits of a species called *Ziziphus lotus*, also known as French or Italian jujubes.

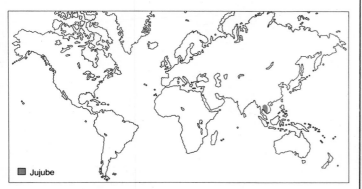
■ Jujube

△ Jujube, 2in (54mm) long

Jujube
(Ziziphus jujuba)
DESCRIPTION: Yellowish, olive-shaped fruit ¾-1¼in (2-6cm) long. The flesh has the consistency of an apple and contains a single pip. Tastes sweet-tart.
COUNTRIES OF ORIGIN: Asia and Europe.
PRODUCER COUNTRIES: Thailand.
AVAILABILITY: August to May.
USE: Eat on its own with the skin, but not the pip. Can also be made into compote, flan filling, etc. In Asia, it is often dried or candied.
KEEPING QUALITIES: A few days at room temperature; about one week in the refrigerator.

NUTRITIONAL VALUE: Not known.
INDUSTRIAL PROCESSING: Dried, candied.

Rosaceae
Strawberry, blackberry, raspberry, loganberry

Although the *Rosaceae* or rose family comprises more than 3,500 species worldwide it is not, as families of plants go, very large if one compares it with the *Compositae*, the family to which the daisy belongs, which boasts some 19,000 species worldwide.

But within the fruit kingdom members of the Rosaceae play a dominant part and their commercial significance is enormous. One reason for this is that many species have a very long history of cultivation and attracted the keen interest of fruit growers and breeders very early on. As a result, there are literally dozens, in some cases even hundreds, of different varieties of apple, pear, plum, cherry, apricot, peach, strawberry and raspberry grown all over the world. Many species of the rose family indigenous to Europe have found homes in all the temperate zones of both hemispheres.

In view of the size and scope of the Rosaceae, we have divided the family into eight sections: strawberries, blackberries, and raspberries; apples; pears; plums; apricots; peaches; cherries; and, finally, miscellaneous.

Strawberries, blackberries, raspberries and loganberries
Wild strawberries grow all over the world, though mainly in Europe, East Asia and North America. The best known European variety is the wood strawberry *(Fragaria vesca)* that flourishes on the sheltered floor of woodlands, in undergrowth, in hedgerows, etc. Country folk have always gathered and eaten these small, fragant fruits; indeed some gastronomes prefer them to cultivated strawberries. However, up until the last century, the wood strawberry was cultivated on quite a large scale, as a variety called the large forest strawberry *(F. moschata)*.

It may surprise the reader to know that all the cultivated strawberries we enjoy today are not European but American in origin. All of them go back to the Chilean strawberry *(F. chiloensis)* and the Virginian strawberry *(F. virginiana)*, both introduced into Europe in the 17th and 18th centuries. French fruit breeders succeeded in crossing both species and finally, at the end of the 18th century, produced the pineapple strawberry *(F. chiloensis grandiflora)*. In the 19th century and more especially in this century, many more varieties were developed from *F. chiloensis grandiflora;* these and their illustrious parents are widely grown today. Many strawberry varieties, however, are only cultivated locally because their flavour, colour and keeping qualities do not satisfy the needs of a wider market.

The strawberry is not a true fruit like an apple, but a false fruit. What we eat is the swollen fruit receptacle; the actual fruitlets are the small pips on the outside. There are two types of strawberry: one fruits only once per season, the other fruits continuously, or at least until the first sharp frosts. Strawberries are now available all year round thanks in part to the perpetual fruiting varieties, but also to extensive commercial growing in the southern hemisphere. Also, with modern cultivation methods, flowering and fruit setting can be either advanced or delayed. Early flowering is achieved by keeping the plants under glass or plastic, and delayed flowering by keeping the plants in cold store and not planting them out until later in the season.

The blackberry *(Rubus fruticosus)* and the raspberry *(R. idaeus)* are closely related species — the fruits of both have a similar composite structure. Blackberries, raspberries and the hybrid cane fruits consist of numerous fruitlets that are, in fact, leaves that have developed a swollen juicy wall on the outside. On the inside, the leaves have hardened to form a little capsule around a cavity, inside which lies tissue attaching the 'fruitlet' to the core or 'hull' of the berry.

Blackberries have only been cultivated since the 1820s, but the varieties that have spread throughout the world are so numerous and so difficult to distinguish from one another that the exact number is unknown. Blackberry experts, however, claim that it is possible to differentiate between some 2,000 separate varieties! Blackberries grow mainly in the northern hemisphere and in mountainous regions of South America. The fruits vary in colour from black to yellow. The Tayberry, a cross between a blackberry and a raspberry, is a newcomer; developed in Scotland and as yet not grown commercially, it has the best qualities of both parents.

The raspberry, too, is indigenous to many countries throughout the world and depending on the variety bears yellow, red, pink, orange, brown or black fruits. The familiar red raspberry that has been commercially grown since the end of the 16th century was mainly the achievement of horticulturists in Greece and Italy. At the end of the 19th century, over 400 different varieties were in cultivation, though the differences between them were very minor. Most of these older varieties have now disappeared, being unsuitable for commercial growing.

The long, burgundy-red loganberry, developed in the United States, is perhaps the queen of the berry fruits. It is a species in its own right and is bigger, juicier and tastier than either a blackberry or a raspberry.

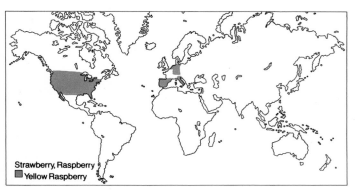

Strawberry, Raspberry
Yellow Raspberry

△ Elvira, 2in (51mm) long

△ Gorella, 2in (49mm) across

Strawberry
(Fragaria sp.)

DESCRIPTION: A false fruit up to 3in (8cm) long (the true fruits are the dozens of pips on the outside) which, depending on the species, can be conical or elongated or almost spherical. The soft, sweet to acid-sweet flesh often has a strong fragrance, especially when ripe. Can be eaten whole.

COUNTRIES OF ORIGIN: Europe and Asia, North America, South America (as far south as Chile).

PRODUCER COUNTRIES: Germany, United Kingdom, Netherlands, Italy, Spain, Israel, United States.

AVAILABILITY: Throughout the year from various producer countries because grown in the open and under glass.

USE: Eat on their own, or with cream and sugar, or make into jam or jelly, or use in cake fillings, fruit salads, ice-cream and milkshakes.

KEEPING QUALITIES: A few days in the refrigerator.

NUTRITIONAL VALUE: 23 Kcal, 60g vitamin C, and traces of vitamin A per 100g serving. Rich in minerals.

INDUSTRIAL PROCESSING: Deep frozen, canned in syrup, jam, juice, compote.

Varieties

Wood Strawberry
(Fragaria vesca)

The best known and most commercial of the 48 wild strawberry varieties, mainly cultivated in France but also exported from Spain and Chile. The fruits are very small compared with those of 'cultivated' varieties, but they are extremely fragrant. Available almost all the year round, but in some seasons can be quite expensive because of transport costs.

El Santa A very recently introduced variety (1984) with remarkably large, deep red fruits and a sweet taste. Not cultivated widely as yet. Mainly suitable for eating fresh.

Elvira A large, shiny, conical, bright red strawberry with firm flesh and a good but slightly bland flavour. 'Elvira' is mainly grown under glass or plastic and is only suitable for eating fresh.

Fletcher Also American and a good variety for freezing. Has medium to large, glossy mid-red fruits of good quality.

Gorella An early variety with large, shiny, bright red, conical fruits (sometimes the point does not ripen). Specimens imported earliest in the year are often rather lumpy and irregular in shape. The flesh is juicy and quite sweet. Grown in many European countries.

Holiday An American variety with large, bright red, glossy fruits which are firm and freeze well. Reasonable flavour.

△ Induka, 1¼in (40mm) long

△ Ostara, 2in (51mm) long   ▽ Primella, 1¼in (32mm) across

Induka A cross between 'Senga Sengana' and 'Puget Beauty'. An early variety with shiny, quite large, darkish-red, conical fruits, often with a pronounced 'waist' at the pointed end. Firm and juicy, and red inside. Strawberry fragrance not very strong.

Ostara A perpetual fruiting variety (i.e. plants bloom and set fruit throughout the summer), and therefore in the shops right up until the beginning of November. Fruits are bright red, rather large, firm, juicy and not over-sweet.

Primella A variety cultivated in Italy and Spain. In northern regions 'Primella' is mainly grown under glass. Rather a pointed shape, deep red outside and light red inside. A firm, sweet, juicy strawberry.

Rabunda Like 'Ostara' a perpetual fruiting variety with light orange to red fruits more or less conical in shape. Flesh is firm, juicy and slightly tart.

△ Sequoia, 2½in (62mm) across   ▽ Tenira, 1⅜in (35mm) across · △ Sivetta, 1⅝in (40mm) across

Tenira A relatively new, rather late ripening variety, a cross between 'Gorella' and 'Red Gauntlet'. Bears firm fruits with a good flavour. Large, conical, deep red and covered with yellow pips. Inside, red and juicy. Strong strawberry scent.

Red Gauntlet The large, conical fruits of this late season variety, widely grown in Scotland, are shiny and bright red or sometimes purple-red in colour, but taste a bit acidic. The flesh is firm and therefore keeps quite well — that is why the variety is sold in such quantities. The taste improves considerably if the rather late fruits are left to ripen fully before picking. May produce a second crop in the autumn, after a good summer.

Sequoia Of American origin, but also grown in Italy and Spain and harvested between April and June. 'Sequoia' is an attractive, rather bulky, deep red or purple-red strawberry with a sweet taste and a delicious smell.

Sivetta Quite a late variety with large, conical, shiny orange-red fruits, and light pink inside. A cross between 'Red Gauntlet' and 'Gorella'. The flavour is unremarkable and without much aroma. The flesh is fairly firm.

Wild Strawberry *(Fragaria indica)* A wild strawberry variety from Asia now also cultivated in South America. The deep pink to purple-red fruits are irregularly shaped, ranging from spherical or flattish to ovoid or conical, but very delicious. They seldom appear on the market but, when they do, are sold as plants rather than as picked fruit.

Blackberry
(Rubus fruticosus)
DESCRIPTION: A compound fruit, consisting of many fruitlets growing around a fibrous 'hull'. Fruits of cultivated varieties are up to 1¼in (3cm) in diameter, and sweeter and more fragrant than wild blackberries, to which they are, of course, related. A large number of cultivated varieties have been developed in the United States.
COUNTRY OF ORIGIN: North America.
PRODUCER COUNTRIES: Germany, United Kingdom, France, Netherlands, United States.
AVAILABILITY: April to October.
USE: Eat fruits on their own or make into jam, jelly, pie fillings, juice, wine, etc.
KEEPING QUALITIES: About three days in the refrigerator.
NUTRITIONAL VALUE: 29 Kcal, 12mg vitamin C, 0.8mg vitamin A per 100g serving. High mineral content.
INDUSTRIAL PROCESSING: Canned in syrup, jam, jelly, juice.

Varieties

Black Satin A variety with a long harvesting season. The fruits are large and shiny black, very juicy and taste reasonably good. They tend to go off quickly.

Himalaya or **Himalaya Giant** An early variety with large, juicy, round or conical fruits, and a pleasant, refreshingly sweet taste though without much aroma. Because they quickly go bad, 'Himalayas' are mainly used for processing.

△ Wild Strawberry, ½in (11mm) across, and El Santa, 1⅖in (36mm) across ▽ Blackberry, 1¼in (32mm) long

Oregon Thornless A late, moderately vigorous variety, with excellent blackberry flavour. Ripens two weeks after 'Himalaya Giant', so sometimes a light cropper. Grown mainly for its flavour and because its lack of thorns makes it easy to manage. Deeply serrated leaves.

Loganberry
(Rubus loganobaccus)
DESCRIPTION: Large, elongated, compound fruit (see 'blackberry'), purple-red in colour, with juicy flesh that quickly goes mushy. Up to 2in (5cm) long. Produced around 1900 by Californian grower J.H. Logan.
COUNTRY OF ORIGIN: United States.
PRODUCER COUNTRIES: United States, New Zealand, United Kingdom.

AVAILABILITY: February to November.
USE: As raspberry.
KEEPING QUALITIES: As blackberry.
NUTRITIONAL VALUE: As blackberry.
INDUSTRIAL PROCESSING: Juice, canned in syrup, jam.

△ Rode Radboud, ½in (16mm) long

Varieties

Malling Promise An early variety with attractive, large, conical fruits, quite soft and with a good taste and aroma. Suitable both for eating fresh and for processing into juice.

Meeker Grown in the United States both for processing and eating fresh. Brighter red than 'Willamette'. A new variety becoming popular with commercial growers. Good flavour.

Munger The main black-fruited variety of raspberry grown in United States. Used for processing, flavouring and in the manufacture of edible dyes.

Rode Radboud A long, conical Dutch variety, dark red in colour, with firm flesh, but little aroma. Suitable for eating fresh or making into juice.

Willamette The most widely grown red respberry in United States. Fruits are large, juicy and burgundy red. Suitable for dessert and processing.

△ Raspberry, ¾in (18mm) long   ▽ Yellow Raspberry, 1in (22mm) long

Raspberry
(Rubus idaeus)
DESCRIPTION: Pink-red to dark red compound fruits, round or slightly conical in shape. The flesh is soft and juicy, sweet and with a characteristic aroma.
COUNTRIES OF ORIGIN: From all over the world.
PRODUCER COUNTRIES: Europe (Netherlands, Germany, Belgium), United States.
AVAILABILITY: June to August.
USE: Eat berries on their own, or with sugar and cream, or make into jam or fillings, or use in fruit salads, ice-cream, milkshakes, etc.
KEEPING QUALITIES: One to two days in the refrigerator.
NUTRITIONAL VALUE: 22 Kcal and 5-30mg vitamin C per 100g serving. Rich in minerals.
INDUSTRIAL PROCESSING: Jam, cordial, juice, canned in syrup, liqueur.

Yellow Raspberry
(Rubus idaeus)
DESCRIPTION: Similar in every way to other raspberry varieties, except that the colour tends to orange. Unlike earlier yellow or orange varieties, the modern yellow raspberry bears fruits of a fairly consistent colour. Not widely or regularly available. The orange colour adds interest to fruit salads.
OTHER INFORMATION: See raspberry.

Fallgold A yellow-fruited American raspberry, cropping in late August/early September. Flavour is mild but sweet.

Rosaceae
Apple

The apple is by far the most important fruit species in the northern hemisphere and is now grown in increasing numbers in the southern hemisphere as well — in Australia, New Zealand, South Africa and South America. Numerically, the apple boasts more varieties than any other fruit species, although we do not know the precise number; some estimates say anywhere between 5,000 and 20,000. What is certain is that the number of varieties is steadily increasing. In recent years dozens of new varieties have been developed and, after satisfactory trials, become available for large-scale commercial growing. They owe their success mainly to characteristics such as high yield and good keeping qualities, but also to fashion — there are fashions in fruit as in almost everything else. Green apples like 'Granny Smith' and 'Golden Delicious' have enjoyed a dramatic increase in favour in recent years.

The apple has been a cultivated fruit for a very long time, probably for longer than the pear. We know this from evidence uncovered in Italy and Switzerland, where remains of cultivated apples that must have been grown a good 4,500 years ago have been found near prehistoric lake dwellings. We are still uncertain about the wild predecessors of the modern apple. The European wild apple *(Malus sylvestris)* probably played only a minor role in the evolution of cultivated varieties. This is also true of the Astrakhan apple *(M. prunifolia)* from Siberia and Northern China and *Malus pumila* from the Caucasus, which still grows in various parts of the Soviet Union.

In virtually all areas where apples are commercially grown, the once familiar tall apple tree has now been largely replaced by trees of dwarf habit. These small trees, which seldom grow much taller than a man, were developed by grafting cuttings of the desired variety onto slow-growing rootstocks. This does not affect the quality of the fruit, but it makes harvesting many times easier. The bushy shape of these smaller trees also ensures even ripening of the fruit. On taller trees, apples on the outer branches ripen first because they get more sun, while those nearer the trunk never colour up as well or taste as sweet.

△ Benoni, 3¼in (84mm) diameter

Apple
(Malus communis)

DESCRIPTION: Depending on the variety, apples can be round, elongated, or flattened, and vary in colour from bright red to 'apple' green. Taste ranges from very tart to very sweet, depending on the variety, and texture can be anything from crisp and juicy to soft and turnipy. Size, too, varies widely. The popular dessert varieties are rarely more than 4in (10cm) across, but there are cooking varieties of much more impressive dimensions.

COUNTRIES OF ORIGIN: Central Asia.

PRODUCER COUNTRIES: All temperate zones.

AVAILABILITY: Throughout the year from all producer countries.

USE: Depending on variety, eat fresh or in fruit salad, or make into apple purée, jam, fillings, or juice, or ferment for cider, or dry as apple rings.

KEEPING QUALITIES: According to variety, anything from one week to many months.

NUTRITIONAL VALUE: Varies from variety to variety, but generally low in fats and oils, and rich in vitamin C.

INDUSTRIAL PROCESSING: Pulp, juice, wine, cider, vinegar, dried, jams.

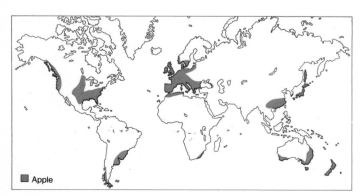

■ Apple

△ Bramley's Seedling, 3in (79mm) diameter ▽ Discovery, 3in (74mm) diameter

Varieties

Benoni An early summer variety, initially green in colour, then ripening to yellow with a red bloom. The apple has a crunchy bite and yellowish flesh. Very juicy and aromatic. An exceptional eating apple, but not suitable for processing. Developed in the mid-19th century in the United States. In the shops from the beginning of September to the end of October.

Bramley's Seedling A popular, large, slightly flattened, sometimes lopsided apple. It is green, though turns yellow and sometimes has a reddish bloom on the side facing the sun. The flesh is hard and white, and the skin is fairly thick. It has a sharp taste and is an excellent cooking apple. Named after the English grower who developed the variety in the 19th century. Available from October to April.

Cox's Orange Pippin Named after an English grower, a Mr Cox from Colnbrook, who raised the variety in about 1830, probably from the pip of a 'Ribston Pippin'. Known as the 'king of eating apples'. Its bite, taste and distinctive aroma have all helped to earn this title. It is a flattish, round, regularly shaped apple, reddish-green in colour, often with a vivid bloom on the side facing the sun, with a whitish-yellow, juicy, crunchy flesh. An excellent eating apple, and also good for juicing.

Delicious Probably the most widely grown apple variety in the world. Originated in United States. Fruits are large and elongated. The skin is thick and green, with a generous red flush. The flesh is yellowish, fairly firm and moderately juicy. Available December to early March.

Discovery An early summer apple available mid-August to mid-September. Skin yellow with a bright red blush. The shape is flattish-round and the flesh is firm and white. It has a somewhat bland flavour. For an early variety it keeps well — for two to three weeks.

Egremont Russet A high quality dessert apple which probably originated in England. Fruits are medium-sized, averaging 2½in (6cm) in diameter, and are more or less round. The skin is yellow but liberally covered with brown russet which is slightly rough to the touch. The flesh is pale yellow, firm, and has the characteristic nutty flavour of russets. Available October to November.

Elstar A new variety obtained by crossing 'Golden Delicious' with other varieties. Large, regularly-shaped and golden-yellow with a red bloom (see picture on page 88). The juicy flesh has a crunchy bite and a pleasant, characteristic aroma. A newcomer that should go far. A variety not so suitable for processing. On the market between November and mid-April.

△ Jonagold (top left), 3¼in (87mm) diameter; Granny Smith (top right), 3in (75mm) diameter; Cox's Orange Pippin (middle), 3in (75mm) diameter; Lombarts Calville (bottom left), 3¼in (82mm) diameter; Elstar (bottom right), 3in (75mm) diameter.

Gloster 69 This variety, of German origin, has been produced by crossing 'Glockenapfel' with 'Red Delicious'. 'Gloster' is a relatively large, longish apple heavily ribbed at the calyx end. The skin is dark to purplish-red; the rather acid flesh is firm, juicy and greenish-white in colour. It is only suitable as an eating apple, and is on the market between November and March.

Golden Delicious This variety was produced at the end of the 19th century in the United States from a natural seedling and then named 'the apple of the future'. It is grown in almost all apple-producing countries and is therefore on the market throughout the year. It is a rather large, sweetish-acid to sweet eating apple with little juice, light green to golden-yellow skin and firm flesh. It does not pulp well, although it is suitable for making juice and cake fillings.

Granny Smith Around the middle of the last century this variety embarked on a world conquest that led from France via Australia and New Zealand to South Africa, South America and then back to Europe. At present it is one of the most popular of all apple varieties. It requires a certain amount of sunshine to ripen properly, and so the number of producer countries is rather restricted. It is a hard green apple, with firm, white, juicy flesh that can be eaten on its own or processed in various ways. It is on the market throughout the year.

Grenadier An excellent early cooking variety widely grown commercially in United Kingdom. Fruits are large, round, flattish and average 3½in (8cm) in diameter. The skin is smooth and pale yellow with russet speckles. The flesh is white, crisp and pleasantly tart. Crops in September and October.

Idared An American cross between 'Jonathan' and 'Wagenerappel'. The fruits are relatively large and uniformly red in colour, sometimes with traces of yellow. The cream-coloured, firm flesh is juicy and slightly acid. An excellent eating apple. It is on the market between October and July.

△ Gloster, 4¼in (110mm) diameter   ▽ James Grieve, 3½in (89mm) diameter   △ Mantet, 4in (97mm) diameter

Lombarts Calville A Dutch variety. When fully ripe, skin is yellow and slightly oily. To meet increased demand for green apples 'Lombarts Calville' is now harvested early so that it can be sold green. It is a large apple with soft, yellowish-white flesh; the taste is slightly acid. Suitable both for eating and processing. Available November to May.

Lord Lambourne A widely grown and popular dessert apple. Fruits are almost round, regular, and 2½in (6cm) in diameter. Ths skin is greenish-yellow with red streaking or flushing on the sunny side. The flesh is also greenish-yellow, soft, juicy and sweet. Available October to November.

James Grieve An eating apple cultivated since the end of the last century and on the market from mid-August to mid-October. On the outside it is yellow with red streaking or flushing, and on the inside yellowish-white. It has several almost identical relatives that are redder and sold as 'Red James Grieve', 'Lired', 'Rubin' and 'Rosamund'. The juicy flesh is delicious, but the flavour can be spoiled if the fruit is harvested too early, as sometimes happens. Unsuitable for processing. Poor keeping quality.

Jonagold A recent cross, produced in the United States, between 'Johnathan' and 'Golden Delicious', and rapidly gaining in popularity as a commercial variety. Often a very large apple, with red streaks or a red bloom on a yellow ground. The flesh is yellowish-white, firm and juicy, and has a pleasant, sweet taste. Equally suitable for eating or processing. Available between October and April.

Mantet An early, tender summer apple of Canadian origin, elongated in shape and tapered towards the calyx. The skin is greenish-yellow with red graining; the flesh is soft and tasty. Available between mid-August and the beginning of September. A related variety is 'Red Mantet' which, as its name implies, has a redder skin.

△ Morgenduft, 3in (81mm) diameter   ▽ Red Delicious, 3½in (87mm) diameter   △ Schone van Boskoop, 3in (83mm) diameter   ▽ Starking, 4in (99mm) diameter

Morgenduft Grown in Argentina, Italy and southern Germany, 'Morgenduft' also goes under such names as 'Hoary Morning', 'Rome Beauty', 'Gillet's Seedling', 'Imperatore' and 'Rimskaya Krasvita'. It is a flattish apple, greenish-yellow in colour, with a blush or streaking of red (some of its derivatives are bright red). The flesh is white and refreshingly tart, good for eating and for cooking. Available April to December.

Red Delicious A variety of American origin, grown widely in Europe, mainly in France and Italy, and in the United States. The apple has a smooth, dark red skin, sometimes slightly streaked. It is also slightly elongated in shape. The soft white flesh is juicy and aromatic, but quickly goes mushy and tasteless. It does not keep very long. 'Red Delicious' is also known as 'Starkrimson' and 'Richared'. Available throughout the year, but peak exports are between February and September.

Schone van Boskoop A Dutch variety, with a skin that can be greenish-yellow, yellow-bloomed or red. Always a large, firm apple with yellow, tart and juicy flesh. A good eating apple, but also suitable for all kinds of processing. Available October to April.

△ Winston, 3in (77mm) diameter ▽ Summerred, 3in (80mm) diameter

△ Yellow Transparent, 3in (72mm) diameter

Tydeman's Early A rather large, regularly-shaped, round apple, ripening to bright red with pale yellow showing through. The soft, juicy flesh is slightly acid. The species puts in a very brief appearance (end August to early September) because it does not keep for long. Not suitable for processing.

Winston A cross, produced in England, between 'Cox's Orange Pippin' and 'Worcester Pearmain'. The greenish-yellow fruits turn orange-red, with faint streaks of red, as they ripen. A large, slightly conical apple with crisp, white flesh and a good flavour. 'Winston' is not suitable for processing, but does keep well. Available between November and May.

Yellow Transparent A very early eating and cooking variety introduced into France from Russia during the last century. Available from mid-July to early August. A handsome, somewhat angular apple with yellowish-green skin. The flesh is white, juicy and pleasantly tart. Within three or four days of picking, becomes soft and tasteless and begins to show cracks. Only suitable for eating fresh.

Starking An American variety, also sold under the names 'Double Red Starking', 'Starking Delicious', and 'Top Red'. Not only grown in the United States and Argentina, but also in Italy, Germany, and England. 'Starkings' are typically longer apples than most, and darkish red. The flesh is yellowish-white, juicy, with sweet and tart nicely balanced. This eating apple can be found in the shops virtually throughout the year.

Summerred A cross between 'Golden Delicious' and 'McIntosh'. Large, longish and, if it has had enough sun, deep red in colour. The flesh is firm, white, juicy and full of flavour. A summer apple for eating fresh. Available from early September to mid-October.

Rosaceae

Pear

The ancestry of the pear is as uncertain as that of the apple. Wild pears are still found in parts of Europe, Western Asia and North Africa, and presumably the cultivated species derive from one or more of these wild species. In the first century AD the Romans, judging by written records, already knew and cultivated 30 different varieties.

The most obvious eating characteristic of pears is their 'woodiness', due to the presence of woody 'stone cells' embedded throughout the flesh. These rather gritty cells have been bred out of most modern varieties to improve texture, but in some they are still plentiful, more noticeably in stewing pears than in the more juicy eating pears.

Up until the 16th century pears were used only for cooking — they were stewed or baked. Documents from the 15th century record that stewed or baked pears were sold on the street and that street vendors frequently bemoaned the fact that they were left with pears unsold at the end of the day. The first eating pears were produced in France and Italy towards the end of the 16th century. Because of their soft, juicy flesh they were later christened *beurré* or 'buttered' pears, a name that still survives in the names of several varieties on the market today, in 'Beurré Hardy' and 'Beurré Alexandra Lucas', for example, both developed in France during the last century.

Cultivated pears only thrive in temperate or subtropical climates. Experiments in the tropics have not been successful because, although the trees survive, they bear inedible fruit, even when planted at altitudes where temperatures compare with those of temperate climates.

Like apples, most modern pear varieties are grown on very small trees; the stately trees that once overtopped two- and three-storeyed houses have now largely disappeared. The rootstock used for these modern trees is the quince, another member of the Rosaceae family (a quince is a fruit halfway between an apple and a pear and is grown, in a limited way, in its own right — see page 119).

There are an estimated 4,000 to 5,000 cultivated pear varieties, many of them recorded in gene banks but only a few of them grown commercially. Almost all modern varieties date from the 18th century.

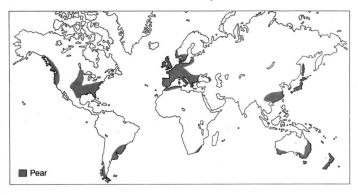

Pear

△ Clapp's Favourite, 4¼in (105mm) long

Pear
(Pyrus communis)
DESCRIPTION: Soft or hard, eating and cooking types, varying in shape from round to long and narrow and sometimes curved, and varying greatly in size. The colour variation is also considerable: greyish-green to dark yellow, sometimes with a red bloom. The flesh of ripe eating pears is soft, juicy and sweet, sometimes with a typical 'acetone' (peardrops) aroma. The flesh of cooking pears is hard and often quite granular. The skin of most eating pears is edible, though it is tougher in some species than in others.
COUNTRIES OF ORIGIN: Central Asia.
PRODUCER: All temperate and sub-tropical countries.

AVAILABILITY: Throughout the year from various producing regions.
USE: Eating pears: peel if desired, and eat on their own, or make into jam, jelly, juice, wine, etc., or use in cakes, fruit salads, ice-creams, etc.
Cooking pears: peel, and simmer or stew with a little sugar for dessert, adding vinegar and spices for chutney or pickle.
KEEPING QUALITIES: Ripe eating pears: a few days. Unripe cooking pears: a few weeks.
NUTRITIONAL VALUE: 42 Kcal and 4mg vitamin C per 100g serving.
INDUSTRIAL PROCESSING: Canned in syrup, juice, jam, wine, liqueur, etc.

△ Beurré Hardy, 4in (100mm) long

Varieties

Abate Fetel A very large, long and often somewhat lumpy pear of French origin but nowadays grown on a large scale in Italy and South Africa. The flesh is juicy and very sweet. Available from September to February (from Europe) and April to June (South Africa).

Anjou One of the most widely grown varieties of pear in United States. Green to yellow-green skin, even when fully ripe. Sweet, spicy and very juicy. Available October to May.

Bartlett or **Williams** Also synonymous with 'Williams Bon Chrétien'. Widely grown in United States and Australia for canning, but in Europe as a dessert pear. Fruits are fairly large, averaging 4in (10cm) in length. The skin is very tender, yellow and has russet speckles and sometimes a tinge of red. Flesh is white, very juicy and sweet.

Beurré Hardy A rather large, russet-skinned eating pear of French origin. The best known of the various Beurré types (*beurré* being French for 'buttered'). The skin is firm, but the flesh is soft, juicy, sweet and mellow. Available from September to mid-November in Europe and the United States. Only keeps for a short time.

Clapp's Favourite Named after the American grower, E. Clapp, this is a large, regularly-shaped, green eating pear with a scarlet blush on the side that gets the sun. The stalk is short and stiff. The flesh is very juicy but has a very faint smell. Only keeps for a short time and is very susceptible to going 'sleepy' (rotting from the inside). Available July to September.

△ Conference, 4¼in (110mm) long

Conference An autumn and winter eating pear of English origin, usually available until April because it keeps well. The fruit is often long and slim due to incomplete fertilization; the skin is yellowish-brown in colour, and sometimes speckled. The flesh is the palest of browns, juicy and sweet; the skin is slightly rough. 'Conference' pears can be eaten raw or baked. Available September to April.

Doyenné de Comice One of the finest eating pears. 'Comice' pears are large and slightly lumpy in shape; the skin is thin, tender and green to yellowish-brown, sometimes with a red blush. The flesh is very juicy, mellow-sweet and fragrant and best eaten raw. Available from the beginning of October to the end of January (in Europe and the United States), and from May to July (from South Africa).

Gieser Wildeman A quite small, brownish-yellow cooking pear of Dutch origin, with a lot of rusty pigmentation on the skin. Varies in length from 1¼-3in (3-7cm). The flesh tends to be soft and grainy and turns pinkish-red when cooked. Available mid-October to late February.

Dr Jules Guyot An early eating pear, grown predominantly in France and Italy and available between August and mid-September. A rather small pear, sometimes irregular in shape. The skin is light green to yellow with a rosy bloom when ripe. The flesh is white and juicy, and granular in the region of the core (where the stone cells are most concentrated). A sweet variety with a slightly musky smell.

Morettini or Moretti A summer eating pear of Italian origin, grown in Italy, France and southern Germany. Largish fruits, yellowish-green in colour with a pretty red bloom. The flesh is yellowish-white, juicy and delicious. Available July to mid-September.

Nelis or **Winter Nelis** A small round pear with much russeted green skin. Widely grown for processing in United States but mainly as a dessert pear in Europe. Available October to May.

△ Gieser Wildeman, 3½in (90mm) long   ▽ Dr. Jules Guyot, 4in (95cm) long

▽ Morettini, 3½in (86mm) long

△ Packham's Triumph, 4in (103mm) long   ▽ Passe Crassane, 4½in (115mm) long   △ Triomphe de Vienne, 4in (106mm) long

Packham's Triumph A pear of Australian origin, now cultivated in Italy, France, United Kingdom, South Africa, United States and South America. A large, rather lumpy eating pear with a green skin that changes to yellow when fully ripe. The juicy flesh has a delicious flavour, though it gets rather grainy around the core. Also very suitable for processing. Available November to August.

Passe Crassane A high quality eating pear of French origin now also cultivated in Italy. A large, chubby fruit with a greenish-brown skin, changing to russet-yellow. The flesh is sweet, with an interesting aftertaste. Juicy, but sometimes contains stone cells around the core. Available mid-September to early March.

Seckel or **Seckle** A very old American dessert variety found growing wild near Philadelphia. Also grown in Europe. The smallest of all pears, 'Seckle' is almost round, and has a yellow skin which flushes red when ripe. The flesh is yellow. Available August to January in United States.

Supertrévoux An eating variety recently developed in the Netherlands; not suitable for processing. A large, fat pear, with a brownish-red bloom on a yellow ground. Keeps for only a short time and so available from mid-August for only three or four weeks. Quickly goes 'sleepy'. The flesh is sweet, provided the pear has not been picked too early.

Triomphe de Vienne A variety of French origin, now mainly grown in France, Belgium, Germany and the Netherlands. It is often very large and can weigh up to 1lb (500g). The fruits are nicely symmetrical, with a green, bronze-speckled skin. Fruits without pips, produced by treating the frosted blooms with gibberellic acid, are slimmer and smaller. The flesh is juicy and sweet, but not suitable for processing. Available September to October.

△ Supertrévoux, 5in (124mm) long

Rosaceae
Plum, cherry plum, damson, sloe

The plum, together with the apricot, cherry, peach and also the almond, belongs to the *Rosaceae* genus *Prunus*, which includes many trees and shrubs that are purely ornamental. The structure of all the *Prunus* fruits is, in fact, similar to that of the individual fruitlets of blackberries or raspberries; the pit or stone inside them is really the hardened inner wall of the ovary, and the fleshy part is the outer wall of the ovary. The seed itself lies inside the pit or stone. Botanists refer to such fruits as 'stone fruits'. Only the seed or kernel of the sweet almond is commonly eaten; in other *Prunus* fruits the kernel is unpleasantly bitter and usually thrown away.

The origin of the plum is even more uncertain than that of the apple or pear. Many European varieties are believed to derive from *Prunus domestica*, a wild plum that grows around the Caspian Sea. Another wild ancestor of both European and South African varieties may have been *P. salicina*, indigenous to China and Japan.

Indeed, it is probable that *P. domestica* and *P. salicina* gave some of their descendants their typical 'nose', or tapering base. American breeders and growers, on the other hand, have made special use of the wild plum *P. subcordiata* indigenous to America, crossing it with plum varieties of European or Asiatic origin.

Popular belief has it that a plum is only ripe if the stalks stays attached to the tree when the fruit is picked. This is not always true.

Like apricots, and to a lesser degree like peaches, some varieties of plum make good dried fruits. Most dried plums or rather prunes sold today come from California and France. The French variety 'Prune d'Agen', rarely available fresh, makes exceptionally delicious prunes because it has a high fructose (fruit sugar) content. Some plum varieties are also used in alcohol distilling; certain kinds of eau-de-vie and schnapps, and the Yugoslavian *slivovitz*, are plum-based.

△ Beauty, 2in (50mm) diameter

Plum
(Prunus domestica)
DESCRIPTION: Round or elongated fruit of widely varying size, up to 4in (10cm) diameter. Colour ranges from greenish-yellow to deep blue-purple. The skin is usually thin and the hard stone lies embedded in sweet, fragrant, soft flesh. The stone is easier to remove from some varieties than others, even when fully ripe.
COUNTRIES OF ORIGIN: Western Asia, Japan and China *(Prunus salicina)*.
PRODUCER COUNTRIES: All countries with a temperate or sub-tropical climate.
AVAILABILITY: Throughout the year from various producer countries.
USE: Eat fresh or make into cake fillings, jam, jelly, juice, wine; preserve in syrup, wine or brandy; some species can also be dried.

KEEPING QUALITIES: A few days.
NUTRITIONAL VALUE: 42 Kcal and 5mg vitamin C per 100g serving.
INDUSTRIAL PROCESSING: Canned in syrup, jam, jelly, compote, dried, distilled.

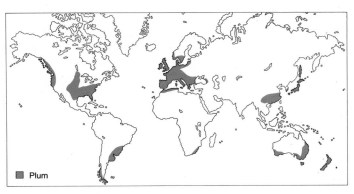

■ Plum

◁ Belle de Louvain, 2¼in (55mm) diameter   △ Burbank, 2in (48mm) diameter

△ Czar, 1½in (40mm) diameter

Varieties

Anna Spáth A late variety, in the shops in October, suitable both for processing and eating fresh. The long, ovoid fruits are bluish-red with a grey-blue bloom. The stone comes out easily. The flesh is yellowish-green and has a reasonable flavour.

Beauty A bright red plum, dark red when fully ripe, which is hot-house grown in Northwest Europe but otherwise chiefly grown in South Africa and the United States. The flesh is light red and usually very juicy; in some growing areas however the fruit is firmer and contains less moisture. Usually available late May to early July.

Belle de Louvain An older plum of Belgian origin with large, ovoid, purplish-blue fruits. The flesh is firm, very juicy and yellowish-green in colour, but tastes somewhat insipid. Available from mid-August.

Burbank An American variety, cultivated mainly in the United States, Japan, Chile, South Africa and Italy. The colour is light red, the taste sweet.

Czar A plum with reasonable flavour and a stone which comes away from the fruit easily. The fruits are small, oval in shape and purplish-blue in colour; the flesh is greenish-yellow. Chiefly grown in the Netherlands, England, Sweden and Germany, and mainly used for cooking. Available in August.

Gaviota An attractive, bright red, heart-shaped plum with deep yellow flesh and an excellent flavour. 'Gaviota' comes from Italy, but is now mainly grown in the United States and South Africa. Available January to March (South Africa) and June to August (United States).

△ Opal 1½in (38mm) diameter   ▽ June Blood, 1¾in (42mm) diameter

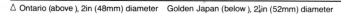

△ Ontario (above), 2in (48mm) diameter   Golden Japan (below), 2¼in (52mm) diameter

Golden Japan A golden-yellow, round plum with a pointed tip. The flesh is yellow and very juicy, but can be tart around the stone, which comes away easily. 'Golden Japan' is cultivated in the United States, France, Italy, and South Africa. It is available from January to May and from June to August.

Harry Pickstone This attractive variety, which is grown mainly in South Africa, comes on the market in February and March. The fruit often has a pointed tip, indicating a cross with the Japanese wild plum. The flesh is golden-yellow, very sweet and has a delicious fragrance.

June Blood A plum of American origin, grown in the United States and to a limited extent in Northern Europe. A delicious, light red plum, juicy and fragrant. Available end June/early July.

Kelsey A rather large, firm fruit with a 'nose', varying in colour from golden-yellow with a red bloom through orange to yellowish-brown. The yellow flesh is firm and delicious. Although thought to be of French origin, 'Kelsey' is now mainly grown in the United States and South Africa.

△ Reine-Claude d'Althan, 1¾in (45mm) diameter ▽ Monsieur Hâtief, 1¾in (45mm) diameter △ Reine-Claude d'Oullins, 1⅘in (46mm) diameter

Monsieur Hâtief A long-established French species, also sold under other names ('Du Roi', 'Orleans'). It is a beautiful, large, oval-round fruit, has a purple skin with greyish speckling, and has sweet and juicy yellow flesh. The stone comes away easily. Available mid-August to late September.

Ontario A round, greenish-yellow plum with a rather deep seam; sometimes the fruits have a pinkish tinge. The flesh is very sweet and juicy, the stone comes away easily but the skin is rather tough. Available July to September from the United States, Belgium, Germany, England, Netherlands.

Opal A rather large fruit, with a skin which is purple on yellow. The sweet, juicy flesh is yellowish-green and comes away easily from the stone. 'Opal' is mainly grown in the Netherlands, Germany and Sweden, and has gained in popularity in recent years. On the market in August.

Redgold A fairly new variety from South Africa, on the market in February/March. The fruits are almost round, tomato red with yellow veining. Juicy and sweet.

Reine-Claude d'Althan A plum of 19th century Czech origin, derived from 'Reine-Claude' (see page 102). The fruit is quite large, round, reddish-purple, and often has a heavy bloom. The flesh is golden-yellow, juicy, sweet and full of flavour, and comes away from the stone easily. Available from end August.

Reine-Claude d'Oullins A large, round plum with a tough skin, green to golden-yellow, with two patches of red near the stalk. The taste is excellent, provided the fruit ripens long enough on the tree. The stone does not come away from the flesh too easily. The fruits turn brown quickly and burst easily. Available in August.

△ Reine-Claude, 1½in (37mm) diameter

Reine-Claude This is the well-known greengage. Probably the oldest variety in the 'Reine-Claude' group, dating back to before the 16th century. Said to be named after Claude, the consort of King François I of France. A rather small, round fruit, bright green to yellow in colour, very soft and juicy, with a honey-sweet taste and fragrance. The stone comes away from the flesh easily. 'Reine-Claude' is grown chiefly in Belgium, France, England and Spain, and is often canned in syrup and made into compote and jam. Available in August and September.

Victoria One of the most highly commercialized plum varieties, chiefly because it can be kept for a limited time in cold storage. The excellent flavour of this large, elongated, red plum can be spoiled by gum formation, particularly around the stone, and failure to thin out heavy cropping. Available in the second half of August.

Santa Rosa A plum of American origin, now cultivated mainly in France, Italy, Spain and South Africa. 'Santa Rosa' has a purplish-red skin and juicy, tasty, red flesh from which the stone is sometimes difficult to remove. Unripe fruits are often on the tart side. 'Santa Rosa' is excellent for processing. It is available December to February (South Africa) and June to November (other producing countries).

Songold A large, South African plum with a 'nose', golden-yellow with a red bloom when ripe. The flesh is orange-yellow and very juicy. On the market in February and April.

△ Victoria, 2in (47mm) diameter   ▽ Songold, 2¼in (61mm) diameter

Cherry Plum or **Myrobalan**
(Prunus cerasifera)
DESCRIPTION: Small, yellow or red cherry-sized fruits. The stone easily comes away from the flesh, which is sweet and juicy.
COUNTRIES OF ORIGIN: Western Asia, Eastern Europe.
PRODUCER COUNTRIES: France, Italy, Belgium, Netherlands.
AVAILABILITY: September.
USE: Eat fresh or use in fruit salads, compote, preserves, wine, etc.
KEEPING QUALITIES: A few days.
NUTRITIONAL VALUE: Not known.
INDUSTRIAL PROCESSING: Jam, jelly, canned in syrup, candied, distilled (eau-de-vie).

Switzen or **Quetsh**
DESCRIPTION: Deep purple, oval fruits with firm, spicy-sweet yellowish-green flesh; not particularly juicy. Approximately 2½in (7cm) long and with a stone that comes away from the flesh easily. There are various varieties of Switzen, all very similar and mostly used in cooking.
COUNTRIES OF ORIGIN: Asia.
PRODUCER COUNTRIES: Germany, France, Netherlands.
AVAILABILITY: September and October.
USE: Can be eaten fresh if very ripe and sweet, but mostly used for jam manufacture, cake filling and bottling.
KEEPING QUALITIES: A few days.
NUTRITIONAL VALUE: Not known.
INDUSTRIAL PROCESSING: Jam, jelly, distilled.

Damson
(Prunus insititia)
DESCRIPTION: Cultivated form of wild plum or bullace, approximately 1in (25mm) long. Intense flavour, but not very juicy. Excellent for making jam and 'damson cheese', a solid preserve of damsons and sugar.
COUNTRIES OF ORIGIN: Asia.
PRODUCER COUNTRIES: Northwest Europe (on small scale).
AVAILABILITY: August.
KEEPING QUALITIES: Two or three days when ripe.
NUTRITIONAL VALUE: Rich in

△ Cherry Plum, 1in (21mm) diameter ▽ Switzen, 1½in (37mm) diameter

vitamin C.
INDUSTRIAL PROCESSING: Jam.

Sloe
(Prunus spinosa)
DESCRIPTION: Fruits of the sloe or blackthorn. Blue-black, very sour, ½-¾in (1-2cm) long, with a relatively large stone. Grows wild in hedgerows and on heathland throughout Western Europe.
COUNTRIES OF ORIGIN: Central Europe, Asia.
AVAILABILITY: October and November.

USE: Inedible fresh, but can be made into jelly (with apple juice), or juice. Also used to flavour gin. Flowers dried and used as 'tea'.
KEEPING QUALITY: A few days.
NUTRITIONAL VALUE: Rich in vitamin C.

Rosaceae
Apricot

The apricot, *Prunus armeniaca*, has travelled an enormous distance from its origins in East and Central Asia to the orchards of California, which now produce more than one fifth of all the apricots grown every year. We know from ancient Chinese records that apricots were cultivated in China at least 4,000 years ago.

Apricots grow on trees 10-13ft (3-4m) high and flourish in most areas that have a Mediterranean climate. Some people believe that the Latin name *armeniaca* points to Armenia as the species' country of origin, but this is incorrect. Armenia, where indeed many apricots used to be cultivated, was probably only a intermediate station along the dispersion route of the plant in the direction of Europe. No wild apricots grow in Armenia, though they certainly do in various East Asian countries including China.

As far as can be ascertained, the cultivated apricot reached the Mediterranean (Greece and Italy) around 100 BC. Its presence was recorded at the beginning of the 17th century in what was then an almost sub-tropical southern England and by the start of the 18th century it had arrived in North America. As early as 1629, Captain John Smith was describing the blooming apricot trees he saw in what was to become the American state of Virginia. These were probably seedlings that had run wild, grown from stones thrown away by Spanish or Portuguese sailors.

Commercial cultivation of apricots is virtually restricted to sub-tropical regions. Apricot trees will grow in cooler regions, but due to early blossoming (in March in the northern hemisphere) the flowers are generally destroyed by frost. Even if this does not happen, in cooler climates the number of hours of sunshine during ripening is usually insufficient to produce palatable fruits. Apricots harvested before they are fully ripe are cotton-woolly and tasteless. This presents problems for growers. For this reason a large part of the apricot harvest is dried or industrially processed in some way.

Although a number of apricot varieties have been developed, they are not easy to distinguish from one another. One way of telling is to look for the country of origin, which must now be displayed on all packing cases and boxes.

△ Hungarian Yellow, 2in (51mm) diameter

Apricot
(Prunus armeniaca)
DESCRIPTION: Round, oval or slightly flattened fruit, up to 3in (8cm) long, varying in colour from pale yellow to orange, often with a red blush on the side facing the sun. The flesh is firm, not over-juicy, and inclined to be fibrous. Flavour depends on ripeness and the variety. When ripe, the stone comes out easily.
COUNTRY OF ORIGIN: China.
PRODUCER COUNTRIES: France, Italy, Spain, Greece, Hungary, United States, South Africa, New Zealand.
AVAILABILITY: Throughout the year, peaking between July and September.
USE: Eat fresh if desired (the skin can be easily removed by brief soaking in hot water), or make into jam, juice, purée, or wine.

KEEPING QUALITIES: About one week at room temperature; very ripe fruits should be used immediately.
NUTRITIONAL VALUE: 51 Kcal, 2700 i.u. vitamin A, and 10mg vitamin C per 100g serving.
INDUSTRIAL PROCESSING: Jam, compote, juice, dried.

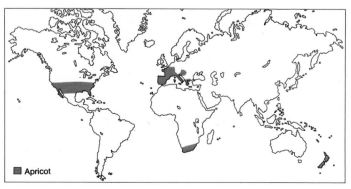

■ Apricot

△ Mario de Cenad, 1½in (41mm) diameter   ▽ Imola Royal, 2in (51mm) diameter

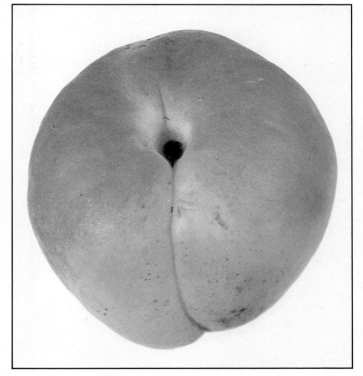

Hamidi A variety originally from Tunisia but now cultivated in Greece. 'Hamidi' is pale yellow, and has a delicious flavour, although the flesh is not very juicy. Appears on the market late May/early June.

Hungarian Yellow A golden-yellow apricot, exported on a large scale in July and August. The skin has a faint flush on the side facing the sun, and the flesh is firm, and very juicy and delicious. Because of its firmness 'Hungarian Yellow' is easy to transport, and very suitable for processing into jam and compote. Cultivated mainly in Southern Germany, Austria, Italy and Greece.

Imola Royal One of the most important Italian apricot varieties, derived from the same stock as the 'Royal' (see page 106). 'Imola Royal' is a large, asymmetrical, elongated apricot, orange-yellow in colour, with a beautiful pink blush on the side facing the sun. The flesh is also orange-yellow; it is juicy and sweet and has a pronounced fragrance. Very suitable for processing beause of the firmness of its flesh. Available in June and July, not only from Italy but also from Spain and Israel.

Mario de Cenad and **Jitrenka** Both varieties are exported from Czechoslovakia and Romania in August, but are seldom sold under these names. Both are almost spherical, yellow-skinned with a tinge of pink. Suitable for processing and for eating fresh.

Varieties

Bebekou The most important Greek export variety, available mid-June to end July. 'Bebekou' is an attractive, round or flattish-round fruit, yellow in colour with only a hint of red. The stone comes away easily from the juicy, sweet flesh. Suitable both for processing and eating fresh.

Bergeron A late apricot (early August) from the Rhône valley in France, large, and with an orange-yellow skin with a faint blush. It has an irregular shape, but the quality is good: juicy, delicious flesh, and the stone comes away easily. Suitable both for eating and processing.

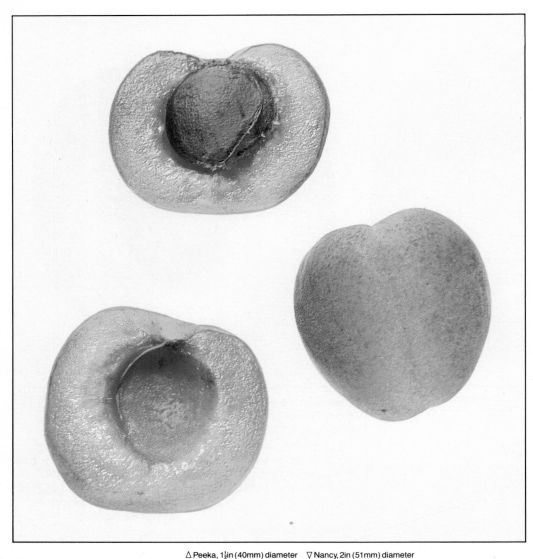

Nancy A very old, French variety, also grown in Italy and Greece, which has played an important part in the improvement of the apricot. The fruits are oval, large, juicy, and of excellent flavour, suitable for eating fresh and for processing. On the market in June and July.

Peeka A new variety, mainly exported from South Africa and New Zealand, which appears in the shops in March and April. Currently being used in experiments to improve the quality of other varieties. 'Peeka' is a flattish, round, orange-yellow apricot, with a stone that comes away easily.

Royal, Perfection and **Goldrich** Three related species ('Perfection' and 'Goldrich' are American improvements of the original French 'Royal') at the present time cultivated in the United States, New Zealand and France. The fruits are round or slightly oval, with a golden yellow skin, and are specially suitable for eating fresh. They are available December to March (from New Zealand), and May to August (from United States and France).

△ Peeka, 1¼in (40mm) diameter   ▽ Nancy, 2in (51mm) diameter

Montedoro An Italian apricot with large, oval fruits of incomparable flavour; it would be a shame to eat them any other way but fresh. Available July and August.

Tirynthos An early Greek variety (exported end of May/June), pale yellow in colour with firm, delicious flesh. Not particularly suitable for processing.

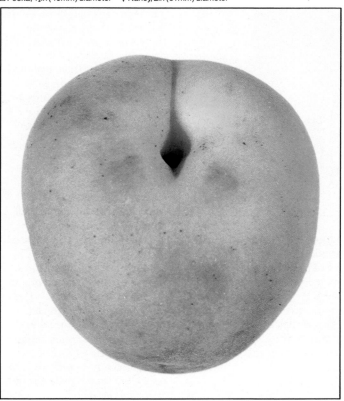

Rosaceae
Cherry, morello cherry, capulin cherry

Fruits of the *Rosaceae* family have been cultivated for centuries, but we really know very little about the origins of some of them. This is particularly true of the cherry. There are, broadly speaking, two kinds of cherry: sweet cherries *(Prunus avium)* and acid or 'morello' cherries *(P. cerasus)*. Sweet cherries probably came from the region between the Black Sea and the Caspian Sea, and acid cherries from the region between the Swiss Alps and the Adriatic. On the other hand, Chinese records of around 2000 BC describe a fruit which sounds exactly like a cherry, so some people think it may have come to Europe from China via Russia and the Middle East. We do know that the Greeks and Romans cultivated and improved cherries. Today they are grown in nearly all countries with temperate climates. Cherries used to be grown in large quantities in Northern Europe, but due to high labour costs and their vulnerability to splitting (caused by irregular water supply), they are now mainly grown in Southern Europe. Cherries are grown extensively in North America.

Cherries grow on large trees, smaller bush-type trees having proved unsatisfactory. But the size of the trees makes it difficult to tend and pick them. Not all the cherries on a single tree ripen at the same time.

There are at least 600 distinct varieties of cherry, but only a few are used to any extent by commercial growers. At least 65 per cent of the crop goes for processing.

When buying cherries, always make sure the stalks are still attached. If not, the fruit may well have been attacked by rot or mildew during shipment or distribution.

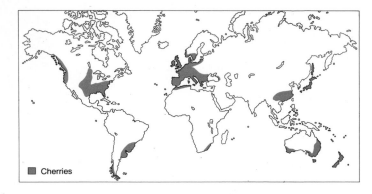

Cherry-growing in Switzerland, a family business.

Cherries

Cherry (sweet)
(Prunus avium)

DESCRIPTION: A round fruit, ½-1in (15-25mm) in diameter, with a stone approximately ¼in (6mm) in diameter. The colour of the fruit depends on the variety. It may be black, purple, bright red, pale yellow tinged with red, or orange-yellow. The colour will depend upon the variety.

COUNTRIES OF ORIGIN: Western Asia.

PRODUCER COUNTRIES: Almost all temperate regions.

AVAILABILITY: End May to end September.

USE: Eat fresh or make into jam, jelly, juice, wine; use in tarts and fillings, desserts, ice-cream, etc.

KEEPING QUALITIES: At room temperature, two days; in the refrigerator, up to six days.

NUTRITIONAL VALUE: 70 Kcal, 110 i.u. vitamin A, and 10mg vitamin C per 100g serving.

INDUSTRIAL PROCESSING: Juice, jam, jelly, fruit drinks, syrup, distilled.

△ Early Rivers, 1in (23mm) across

Varieties

Burlat An old European species that has spread throughout the world and is now grown in almost all cherry-producing countries, particularly in California. The 'Burlat' is a large, shiny, firm cherry, light to dark red in colour with sweet, juicy, yellow flesh. Equally suitable for eating fresh and for processing. Available end May and early June.

Early Rivers An early and very popular cherry, chiefly grown in Germany and United Kingdom, formerly known as the 'German Cherry'. The fruits are quite large, light red to brownish-red in colour, with soft, sweet, juicy flesh.

Japanese Yellow This 'multi-coloured' cherry (yellow tinged with red) like 'Napoleon', and is chiefly used for industrial processing. Grown in Belgium, Germany and Netherlands. Available July and August.

△ Japanese Yellow, 1 in (23mm) across   ▽ Burlat, 1 in (21mm) across

Lambert and **Bing** These are the most widely grown varieties in the United States, where they originated. 'Lambert' has a slightly shorter stalk than 'Bing'. Both are red-black, firm and juicy, and have a delicious flavour. 'Lambert' is available first, from late June to mid-July, and the 'Bing' season extends into August.

△ Schneiders Späte Knorpelkirsche, 1 in (25mm) across. ▽ Meikers, 1 in (19mm) across

Meikers An old Dutch variety written about as early as the 17th century. A cross between sweet and acid varieties (see 'Morello'). The variety is harvested in June. It is a moderately large, light to dark red cherry, juicy and with a refreshingly acid taste and a strong scent.

Napoléon Bigarreau A firm, yellow cherry tinged with red; the amount of red increases as the cherry ripens. This large, regularly shaped, round cherry has yellowish-white flesh. Not especially suitable for eating fresh; chiefly used for processing, for glacé cherries particularly. Grown in Belgium, France and Italy. Available July and August.

Schneiders Späte Knorpelkirsche One of the largest of all cherry varieties, chiefly grown in Belgium, Germany, and Netherlands. The fat fruits are brown-red in colour and often rather dull; the flesh is crispy, sweet, aromatic and very juicy. On the market in July and August.

△ Trakana, ¾in (17mm) across   ▽ Black Cherry, 1in (21mm) across

Trakana Mainly grown in Southern Germany and Greece. A large, firm, heart-shaped cherry, shiny, and bright to dark red in colour. The flesh is red, sweet and juicy. On the market in June and July.

Black Cherry A very famous variety, blackish-red, and heart-shaped. The flesh is also dark red, and so is the stone. The juice of this variety turns the mouth and lips an alarming purple! The flesh is soft, sweet and juicy. Available in July.

△ Wijnkers, 1 in (27mm) across ▽ Vignola Black, 1 in (25mm) across

Vignola Black A cherry from Italy and Greece, on sale in late May and early June. The fruit is rather large and dark red to black. The flesh is dark, sweet, juicy and fragrant. 'Vignola Black' is mainly an eating cherry.

Wijnkers An old Dutch variety, mainly grown in Belgium and Netherlands, and on the market in late June and early July.

△ Morello Cherry, ¾in (18mm) across

Morello Cherry
(Prunus cerasus)
DESCRIPTION: Soft, round cherry, sometimes lopsided, approximately 1¼in (3cm) in diameter, red to dark red in colour and with red flesh. The most important difference between 'Morello' cherries and 'sweet' varieties is the taste: 'Morello' is so acid that it is only suitable for eating fresh when fully ripe. This applies particularly to the fruits of the second harvest of each year, known as 'latecomers'.
COUNTRIES OF ORIGIN: Southeast Europe.
PRODUCER COUNTRIES: Throughout Western Europe.
AVAILABILITY: July and August.
USE: Only eat fresh when fully ripe; otherwise make into juice, jam, or fillings, or preserve in syrup or alcohol.

KEEPING QUALITIES: As sweet cherry.
NUTRITIONAL VALUE: As sweet cherry.
INDUSTRIAL PROCESSING: As sweet cherry.

Capulin Cherry
(Prunus salicifolia)
DESCRIPTION: A wild cherry from Central America, ½-1in (1-2cm) in diameter, dark red in colour, with a spicy flavour.
COUNTRIES OF ORIGIN: Central America.
PRODUCER COUNTRIES: Mexico and Guatemala.
AVAILABILITY: March and April.
USE: Eat fresh or process as sweet cherry.
KEEPING QUALITIES: As sweet cherry.

Rosaceae
Peach, nectarine

The Latin name for the peach tree, *Prunus persica*, is misleading — the peach does not come from Persia but from East Asia, like the apricot. One explanation of the Latin name is that the Romans first encountered the fruit in Persia, or were aware that their predecesssors, the Greeks, had come across the fruit there. But none of this is very certain.

The peach has followed approximately the same dispersion route as the apricot and is at present grown commercially in much the same areas as the apricot. Peaches can withstand a cooler climate than apricots, but in cooler regions they often have to be grown in conservatories or greenhouses — the costs of cosseting peaches in this way usually prohibits commercial growing. Peaches grown in the open need a certain number of hours of summer sunshine to ripen properly, even if winter temperatures hover around freezing point. Peaches are often picked unripe and will post-ripen at room temperature, but the taste suffers accordingly. The skin of a ripe peach peels off easily, and the stone virtually rattles around inside. Depending on the variety, the flesh can be yellow or greenish-white.

The peach has a slightly furry, downy skin. Depending on the variety, skin colour can vary from pale yellow — which does not necessarily mean the fruit is unripe — to golden-yellow with a red blush that invades almost the entire surface of the fruit when it is fully ripe.

Nectarines look a little different from peaches. They have a completely smooth skin, more vivid colouring — bright red and yellow — and are generally smaller. Contrary to popular belief, a nectarine is not a cross between a peach and a plum. It is a spontaneously occurring variant of the peach, and can be propagated by grafting and other methods. Peaches and nectarines are genetically equivalent, which is why a peach tree can sometimes grow from a nectarine stone, and *vice versa*.

The nectarine — like the peach — originally came from Asia. However, a similar mutation occurred in France in the 17th century, and was christened *brugnon*. Nectarines account for approximately 25 per cent of total peach production. Telling the difference between various varieties is a matter for experts.

△ Dixi Red, 2½in (67mm) in diameter

Peach
(Prunus persica)

DESCRIPTION: Round, sometimes slightly elongated fruit, up to 5in (12cm) in diameter, with a thin, downy skin and a marked 'seam'. The flesh, depending on the variety, is orange-yellow or greenish-white, very juicy and aromatic when ripe; the white-fleshed varieties are sometimes the more fragrant. The flesh is sometimes fibrous and streaked with red where it meets the large, corrugated stone.

COUNTRIES OF ORIGIN: China, Japan.

PRODUCER COUNTRIES: France, Italy, Spain, Greece, Israel, United States, South Africa, Australia.

AVAILABILITY: Throughout the year, peaking between July and September.

USE: Peel and eat fresh, or make into jam, compote, fillings, etc., or use in fruit salads and other desserts, or use to garnish meat and fish dishes; can also be dried, preserved in syrup or brandy, made into jams and chutneys, or distilled into liqueur.

KEEPING QUALITIES: Two to three days at room temperature when ripe.

NUTRITIONAL VALUE: 38 Kcal, 1,330 i.u. vitamin A, and 7mg vitamin C per 100g serving.

INDUSTRIAL PROCESSING: Juice, canned in syrup, jam, compote, dried, distilled (eau-de-vie).

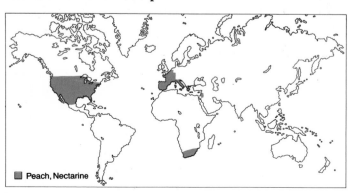

■ Peach, Nectarine

△ Amsden, 3in (75mm) diameter   ▽ Coronet, 3in (75mm) diameter

Varieties

Amsden A medium-sized, almost spherical peach with a bright colour and a velvety skin. The whitish flesh has an excellent flavour. Main producer countries are Italy, Israel, South Africa and United States. Greenhouse specimens generally have a softer skin, pulpier flesh and sometimes a nub on the end opposite the stalk. Available mid-May to mid-June and from November to January.

Cardinal An American variety, also grown in France, Italy and Spain. A large peach, slightly oval, with yellow skin flushing to orange-red on the side that faces the sun. The flesh is light yellow, juicy and tastes good. Available early June.

Coronet An American species, mainly grown in United States, France, Italy, and South Africa. An attractive, orange-yellow streaked, almost spherical peach with pale to dark yellow flesh that is very soft, juicy and fragrant. The stone comes away easily. In the shops end June to end July, and November to January (from South Africa).

Dixi Red A variety of American origin that has now travelled to almost all peach-growing countries. Available late May to August, and from November to January. A flattish peach with yellow, firm, very juicy flesh, good for eating fresh and for processing.

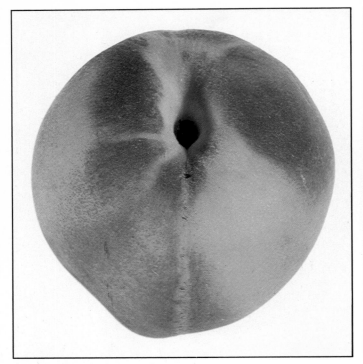

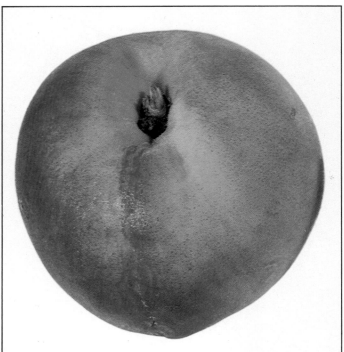

△ Junegold , 3¼in (82mm) diameter   ▽ Early Red, 3in (74mm) diameter

△ Redhaven, 3in (75mm) diameter   ▽Springcrest, 2½in (65mm) diameter

Early Red An early species, chiefly grown in Spain, and seen in the shops in May. 'Early Red' is a pale yellow peach with a red bloom. The flesh is yellow and juicy. This variety is susceptible to 'hollow stone' — the stone splits while it is still in the fruit. Mould can develop in the cavity, making the fruit worthless.

Junegold A golden-yellow, oval peach produced in the United States, with an orange-red bloom, and firm, juicy, aromatic, yellow flesh. Also grown in France, Italy and Greece. Available in June and July. Equally good for eating fresh and for processing.

Redhaven A peach of American origin, now well established in almost all peach-producing countries. Typefied by an orange-yellow skin with a deep orange tinge on the side that faces the sun. The flesh is yellow, juicy and delicious. Exported July and December.

Springcrest An early species grown mainly in Spain and available from May onwards. An attractive peach, almost spherical and a rich dark red in colour. The flesh is juicy and full of flavour. Also susceptible to 'hollow stone' (see 'Early Red').

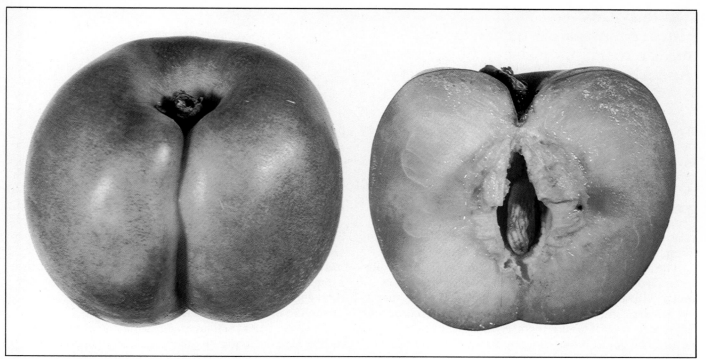

△ Armking, 3in (75mm) diameter ▽ Independence, 2in (57mm) diameter

Nectarine
(Prunus persica)

DESCRIPTION: The nectarine is a natural mutation of the peach and is very similar to it, except that the skin is smooth and shiny. It is not a cross between a peach and a plum as is sometimes asserted.

OTHER INFORMATION: As peach, but no need to peel.

Varieties

Armking An early variety from France, Spain and Italy, more or less spherical, with a deeply indented seam, and often on the pale side. Predominantly yellow with only faint blushing. The flavour is not exceptional. Exported in the second half of June.

Independence A red and yellow nectarine with firm, yellow flesh that is not only juicy and full of flavour but also has a fragrance quite its own. The stone comes away easily from the flesh. 'Independence' is of American origin and is mainly grown in United States, France and Italy (June and July) and Chile (December to March).

Nectared 4 A variety grown very widely in France and Italy, three-quarters red and a quarter yellow. The flesh is yellow and often red around the stone; it is sweet, juicy and of excellent eating quality. The stone comes away easily. Available July and August.

Rosaceae
Cocoa plum, azarole, quince, loquat, medlar, rose hip, wineberry, boysenberry, Andes berry, rowanberry, serviceberry

Apart from the commercial heavyweights of the rose family described in the preceding pages, there are numerous other members of the family of lesser reputation and more local distribution which deserve mention. Many of these have been on the market in a small way for centuries or have been traditionally picked from hedgerows and coppices by country folk. Others are relative newcomers and only sporadically available in the West, and then only in specialist shops.

The hard-fleshed quince (*Cydonia oblonga*), originally from Cydonia, a town on the north coast of Crete, was much cultivated at one time for use in preserves because it has a high pectin content. Pectin is essential for setting jam made of fruits that do not themselves contain enough pectin. The quince's fall from popularity in recent years is a direct result of the appearance on the market of synthetic

Rose hips are the fruits of various species of rose. They can be harvested by machine and processed to make syrup, jam, juice, and tea.

pectin and of waning interest in home jam-making. The same applies to the medlar (*Mespilus germanica*). Medlars have been grown, picked, eaten and cooked for centuries, but nowadays a medlar tree is a rare sight. Compared with the large, sweet, flavoursome fruits the modern palate insists upon, medlars are an acquired taste.

Rosaceae fruits, such as the azarole (*Crataegus azarolus*), the rose hip (*Rosa canina*), the wineberry (*Rubus phoenicolasius*), the rowanberry (*Sorbus aucuparia*) and the serviceberry (*Sorbus domestica*) are not often seen in shops or markets today, not even in country markets, but they are still eaten. Demand is not great enough to make commercial growing viable.

Rosaceae fruits that have been gaining in popularity recently are the loquat or Japanese medlar (*Eribotrya japonica*), the Andes berry (*Rubus glaucus*) and the boysenberry (*Rubus ursinus*). Loquats now grow in various sub-tropical countries — commercial varieties include 'Tanaka', 'Advance', 'Champagne', 'Premier' and 'Early Red'. The Andes berry and boysenberry are attracting the interest of a growing number of fruit growers, although their commercial qualities are still being developed. The cocoa plum (*Chrysobalanus icaco*), on the other hand, is the fruit of a bush from tropical America and Africa and only appears in specialist shops from time to time, more as a curiosity than as a response to demand.

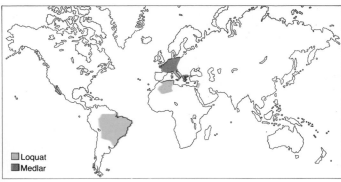

Loquat
Medlar

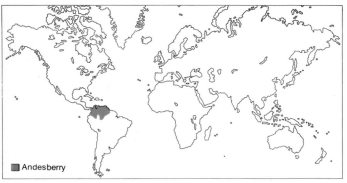

Andesberry

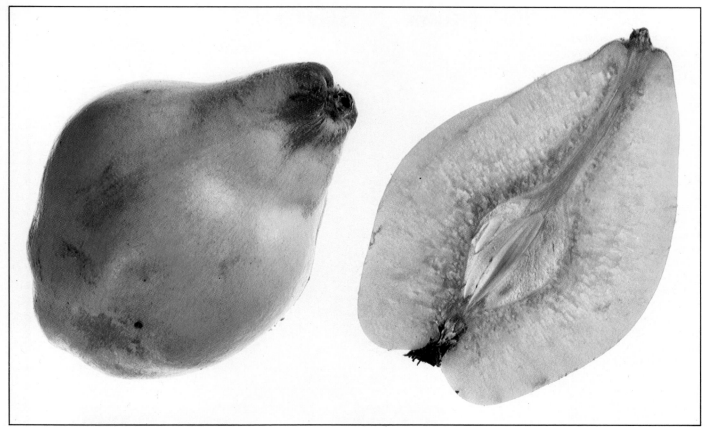

△ Quince, 5in (120mm) long

Cocoa Plum
(Chrysobalanus icaco)
DESCRIPTION: Oval, plum-shaped fruit with a smooth skin and a very large stone. The colour varies from yellowish-white to very dark red. The white flesh usually tastes bitter or a little tart, probably because the fruits are seldom imported ripe.
COUNTRIES OF ORIGIN: Central and South America.
PRODUCER COUNTRIES: Central America, some African countries.
AVAILABILITY: June, and October to December.
USE: Eat ripe fruits fresh, or make into jam, compote, fillings, etc., or bottle in syrup.
KEEPING QUALITIES: One week at room temperature.
NUTRITIONAL VALUE: Not known.
INDUSTRIAL PROCESSING: None.

Azarole
(Crataegus azarolus)
DESCRIPTION: A small, apple-shaped fruit $\frac{1}{4}$-1$\frac{1}{4}$in (1-3cm) in diameter. As the fruit ripens the skin changes colour from pale white through yellow to red. There are several small pips. Sour taste.
COUNTRIES OF ORIGIN: Asia.
PRODUCER COUNTRIES: Countries around the Mediterranean.
AVAILABILITY: August, September.
USE: Not suitable for eating fresh, but can be made into jam and jelly, or used to make juice or wine.
KEEPING QUALITIES: About one week at room temperature.
NUTRITIONAL VALUE: Not known.
INDUSTRIAL PROCESSING: None.

Quince *(Cydonia oblonga)*
DESCRIPTION: Knobbly fruits, elongated and pear- or apple-shaped. The downy skin is greenish- to dark yellow and sometimes covered with rusty blotches. The flesh is yellow, sour, dry and very hard but also very fragrant. The core contains a lot of pips, sometimes as many as 20 per compartment.
COUNTRIES OF ORIGIN: Western Asia (Iran, Turkey).
PRODUCER COUNTRIES· France, Italy.
AVAILABILITY: July to April.
USE: Not suitable for eating fresh, only for making into jam, jelly, compote, juice, bottling in brandy, etc. The fruit should be thoroughly washed (to remove the down), cut into pieces and simmered slowly for a few hours. The flesh turns red when cooked.
KEEPING QUALITIES: A few weeks, provided fruit is not bruised.
NUTRITIONAL VALUE: Not known.
INDUSTRIAL PROCESSING: Jelly, jam, liqueur (Contignac).

Loquat or Japanese Medlar
(Eribotrya japonica)

DESCRIPTION: A pear-shaped fruit, 1¼-3½in (3-9cm) long and, depending on the variety, pale yellow to deep orange in colour. The skin is thin and delicate. The flesh is orange and juicy, tastes like a mixture of apple and apricot, and contains four to nine largish, shiny pips.

COUNTRIES OF ORIGIN: China and Japan.

PRODUCER COUNTRIES: Italy, Algeria, Israel, Brazil, United States (California).

AVAILABILITY: Throughout the year.

USE: Eat fresh (without the pips), make into jam or compote, or use in fruit salads.

KEEPING QUALITIES: Two days at room temperature.

NUTRITIONAL VALUE: Not known.

INDUSTRIAL PROCESSING: None.

Medlar
(Mespilus germanica)

DESCRIPTION: Rust-brown, distinctly flattened fruit, up to 2in (5cm) in diameter. On the flattened, open underside are the remains of the five flower sepals. The skin is hard and feels rough. The fruit contains five stony pips, so there is not much flesh. The taste is pleasantly spicy, but rather tart.

COUNTRIES OF ORIGIN: East Asia, Balkans.

PRODUCER COUNTRIES: Germany, Netherlands, Belgium, France, Italy, Greece.

AVAILABILITY: November to March.

USE: Contrary to popular belief, medlars do not have to be rotten or 'bletted' before they are suitable for eating. Even so, very hard fruits are best post-ripened until they are soft or have been softened by frost. Wash, boil (with sugar) and press through a sieve before making into jam, jelly, or purée.

KEEPING QUALITIES: Ripe fruits: only a few days.

NUTRITIONAL VALUE: Not known.

INDUSTRIAL PROCESSING: Jelly, compote (often in combination with other fruits).

△ Loquat, 2in (51mm) long ▽ Medlar, 1⅝in (42mm) diameter

Rose Hip
(Rosa ssp.)

DESCRIPTION: Fruits of various rose species (R. canina, R. rugosa), up to 1in (25mm) long and orange to orange-red. Rose hips, which contain masses of seeds, grow in clusters. The taste of raw rosehips is not very pleasant; the scanty flesh is rather insipid.

COUNTRIES OF ORIGIN: Europe and Asia. Some commercial cultivation, but mostly picked wild.

AVAILABILITY: August to November.

USE: Rose hips can be processed to make jam or syrup, or dried, ground and infused in boiling water to make 'tea' (good for the bladder and kidneys).

NUTRITIONAL VALUE: Very high vitamin C content: 800-2900mg per 100g of hips.

INDUSTRIAL PROCESSING: Juice, jams, concentrates for fruit syrup mixtures.

△ Wineberry, ½in (11mm) diameter (average) ▽ Rose Hip, 1⅓in (34mm) across

Wineberry
(Rubus phoenicolasius)
DESCRIPTION: Yellow to tomato-coloured fruits shaped like blackberries. The taste is somewhat tart, with a characteristic aroma.

COUNTRIES OF ORIGIN: China and Japan.

PRODUCER COUNTRIES: United States, Northwest Europe.

AVAILABILITY: August (very sporadic).

USE: As blackberry.

KEEPING QUALITIES: As blackberry.

NUTRITIONAL VALUE: As blackberry.

INDUSTRIAL PROCESSING: None.

Boysenberry
(Rubus ursinus cv. Boysen)
DESCRIPTION: Dark red to black fruits, shaped like a raspberry but considerably longer. Juicy, with a distinctive taste not at all like that of any of the fruits — strawberry, raspberry, loganberry and dewberry — from which it was developed in the 1920s.

COUNTRY OF ORIGIN: United States.

PRODUCER COUNTRIES: United States, New Zealand, Australia.

AVAILABILITY: August to January.

USE: As raspberry and blackberry.

KEEPING QUALITIES: As blackberry.

NUTRITIONAL VALUE: 35mg vitamin C, and traces of vitamins A and B per 100g serving.

INDUSTRIAL PROCESSING: Juice, pulp and jam (in the United States).

121

△ Rowanberries, ⅜in (10mm) diameter

△ Serviceberry, ½in (10mm) diameter

Andes Berry
(Rubus glaucus)
DESCRIPTION: Dark red to black berry, about 1½in (4cm) long, with an especially fine, sweet taste, and a strong aroma. Similar in appearance to the European wild blackberry, but the fruit is much larger.
COUNTRY OF ORIGIN: Colombia.
PRODUCER COUNTRIES: Colombia, Venezuela.
AVAILABILITY: October to February.
USE: As cultivated blackberries; best eaten fresh.
KEEPING QUALITIES: One to two days in the refrigerator.
NUTRITIONAL VALUE: Not known; probably as blackberry.
INDUSTRIAL PROCESSING: Deep frozen, fruit pulp.

Rowanberry
(Sorbus aucuparia)
DESCRIPTION: Fruits of the rowan or mountain ash. Round, apple-shaped fruits, approximately ½in (1cm) in diameter, growing in compact, brilliant orange or red clusters. The bitter flesh contains two or three seeds.
COUNTRIES OF ORIGIN: Europe.
PRODUCER COUNTRIES: Not commercially grown.
AVAILABILITY: August to October.
USE: Make whole fruits into jelly (boil berries in plenty of water, strain the fruits and juice, then boil up the juice with sugar until it thickens). Tea made of dried rowanberries helps settle stomach upsets and is also diuretic.
KEEPING QUALITIES: About two weeks at room temperature.
NUTRITIONAL VALUE: Vitamin C and vitamin A.

Serviceberry
(Sorbus domestica)
DESCRIPTION: A wild species, not commercially grown. Round, apple-shaped fruits, approximately 1in (25mm) in diameter and yellowish-green in colour, with a faint bloom that intensifies as the fruit ripens. Serviceberries grow in sparser clusters than rowanberries. The single stone in each fruit is difficult to remove.
COUNTRIES OF ORIGIN: Southern Europe.
PRODUCER COUNTRIES: France, Belgium, Netherlands.
AVAILABILITY: September to October.
USE: Allow the fruits to ripen after picking or keep for a short time in the deep freeze. The flesh then becomes soft and can be used for purée, compote, game sauce, etc.
KEEPING QUALITIES: About one week at room temperature.

Rutaceae

Casimiroa, wampee, citrangequat, limequat, orangequat, malaquina, ortanique, pomelo, ugli, sambal, lime, Seville orange, bergamot, shaddock, lemon, citron, fingered citron, calamansi, grapefruit, mandarin, orange, kumquat

The *Rutaceae* family comprises some 900 species, most of which grow in the tropics. Only a few genera produce edible fruits. Of these, the genus *Citrus* is the most important, playing a major role in the international fruit trade.

Citrus fruits are probably East Asian in origin, and probably arose from just ten or twelve wild species. Over the centuries, these species have been selected, crossed, improved and re-crossed so many times that the relationships between them are now extremely complicated. Even the experts — botanists and traders, whose business it is to know exactly what they are breeding or selling — have regular disagreements about nomenclature and genetics.

The entire globe is now encircled by a 'citrus belt' within which citrus fruits are cultivated on a very large scale. And, as if there were not enough confusion already, identical varieties tend to vary in colour and taste depending upon local conditions, and local experiments are legion. The citrus belt lies between latitudes 40° North and 40° South. Very little citrus fruit is grown outside these boundaries; inside them grow all those species and varieties that have been found to be commercially valuable.

With the development of modern storage and transport methods after World War II, a network of trade routes spread outwards from the citrus belt to all parts of the world where citrus fruit is eaten. Many citrus fruits are sold under brand names such as Jaffa, Outspan, Sunkist, Maroc, Spania and so on; these are 'umbrella' names for many different varieties, species and even genera.

Citrus fruits can be crossed so easily that new hybrids and new hybrids of hybrids regularly appear on the market. That is why the information in this chapter is offered as an approximate guide only. There are very few *Rutaceae* species on the market that do not belong to the genus *Citrus*.

All citrus fruits have a firm, leathery skin that contains strong-smelling, volatile oils. At one time, it was legal to enhance skin colour artificially, but this is now prohibited in most importing countries. However, various treatments after harvesting are legal and widely practised; such treatments are generally indicated on boxes and wrappings, but the consumer rarely sees these. So if you want to use citrus peel for making marmalade, for example, the fruit should be thoroughly washed first.

Oranges. There are approximately 2,000 orange varieties. Of these, around 100 are cultivated on a large scale. Oranges are usually divided into various categories, the most important being 'blonde' oranges, blood oranges and navel oranges. Oranges from the tropics tend to be a somewhat discoloured; this has nothing to do with dirt or eating quality, but is simply the result of there being no cold nights during the ripening season.

Mandarin oranges. There are three distinct categories in the mandarin group: 'true' mandarins, satsumas and tangerines. There are also various crosses between them and crosses involving grapefruit, oranges and Seville oranges. All mandarin-type oranges are sweet and easy to peel; the fact that some are also seedless has enhanced the general popularity of the group.

Lemons. Although there are various varieties of lemon, they are not easy to tell apart and in the trade there is seldom any effort made to distinguish one lemon from another — 'a lemon is a lemon is a lemon'. There are several citrus fruits closely related to the lemon: the citron, the lime, and the sambal from Southeast Asia.

Grapefruit. The original grapefruit was probably a natural mutation of the shaddock. The name 'grapefruit' is thought to be derived from a variety described in the 19th century as having fruits 'growing in trusses like grapes'. Development has been particularly intensive and successful in the United States, which now supplies 95 per cent of world production. As well as the yellow-fleshed varieties there are now much sweeter pink- and red-fleshed varieties and even a green-skinned variety.

The *Citrus* genus also includes the **kumquat** and its derivatives; the **ugli,** which is probably a cross between a tangerine, a grapefruit and a Seville; the **shaddock,** already mentioned as the ancestor of the grapefruit; the Israeli **pomelo,** a cross between a shaddock and a grapefruit; and a few less well known crosses such as the **malaquina** and the **ortanique.** The two *Rutaceae* fruits which do not belong to the *Citrus* genus are the **casimiroa** and the **wampee.** In the pages which follow, we describe all of these in order of their generic names.

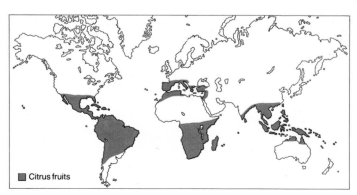

■ Citrus fruits

Casimiroa or Mexican Apple
(Casimirea edulis)
DESCRIPTION: Round, slightly tapering fruit, 2½-4½in (6-12cm) in diameter and yellow to yellowish-green in colour. The skin is very thin. The flesh is soft, yellow-white, tastes sweet with a faintly bitter aftertaste, and has a very characteristic smell. Has up to five yellow, oval pips.
COUNTRIES OF ORIGIN: Central America.
PRODUCER COUNTRIES: Mexico, United States.
AVAILABILITY: July to September, but unreliable as fruit does not travel well.
USE: Eat fresh, with the skin but not the pips, or make into jam or marmalade.
KEEPING QUALITIES: A few days at room temperature.
NUTRITIONAL VALUE: 125 Kcal, 10 i.u. vitamin A, and 20mg vitamin C per 100g serving.
INDUSTRIAL PROCESSING: Jam or marmalade.

Wampee
(Clausenia lansium)
DESCRIPTION: Small, spherical fruits, approximately 1in (25mm) in diameter, with a yellow or yellowish-brown, translucent skin. The tart and thirst-quenching flesh is white and jelly-like and contains up to five green pips.
COUNTRIES OF ORIGIN: China, Vietnam, Cambodia.

PRODUCER COUNTRIES: China, Southeast Asia, United States.
AVAILABILITY: Virtually throughout the year, although irregular.
USE: Eat fresh, use in fruit salads and desserts, or make into jam or fruit juice.
KEEPING QUALITIES: A very short time.
NUTRITIONAL VALUE: Not known.
INDUSTRIAL PROCESSING: Jam, fruit juice, canned in syrup.

Citrangequat, Limequat, Orangequat
(Citrus ssp.)
DESCRIPTION: Crosses between kumquat and citrange (itself a cross between the lemon and the orange), kumquat and lime, and kumquat and orange respectively.
OTHER INFORMATION: See kumquat (page 138).

Malaquina
(Citrus sp.)
DESCRIPTION: A slightly flattened, rather large fruit, approximately 4in (10cm) in diameter, with an easily peeled, brownish-orange skin. The pale orange flesh is sweet and juicy, has a distinct 'mandarin' taste and contains few if any pips. The malaquina is a cross between a mandarin and an orange.
COUNTRY OF ORIGIN: Uruguay.
PRODUCER COUNTRIES: Central and northern South America.
AVAILABILITY: September to December.
USE: As ugli.
KEEPING QUALITIES: One week at room temperature.
OTHER INFORMATION: Not known.

Ortanique
(Citrus sp.)
DESCRIPTION: A large fruit, up to 6in (15cm) in diameter, rather flattened in shape and with a thin, dirty orange-coloured skin. The orange-yellow flesh is sweet and very juicy; the smell is a blend of orange and tangerine, from which it was developed.
COUNTRY OF ORIGIN: Jamaica.
PRODUCER COUNTRY: Jamaica.
AVAILABILITY: February to May.
USE: Press or eat fresh like the ugli.
KEEPING QUALITIES: As ugli.
NUTRITIONAL VALUE: Not known.
INDUSTRIAL PROCESSING: None.

△ Pomelo, 5¼in (136mm) diameter ▽ Ugli, 4¼in (155mm) diameter

Pomelo
(Citrus sp.)
DESCRIPTION: An Israeli cross between the shaddock and the grapefruit. Smaller than the shaddock but larger than the grapefruit. The skin is rather smooth, whitish-yellow, and thickly packed around the pale yellow segments. The pith is bitter, and the flesh rather tart.

COUNTRY OF ORIGIN: Israel.
PRODUCER COUNTRY: Israel.
AVAILABILITY: December to April.
USE: Cut the fruit into quarters from crown to base, and cut out the flesh with a knife. Eat fresh, sweetened with sugar to taste, make into jam or jelly, or add to fruit salads. The peel can be candied.

KEEPING QUALITIES: About two weeks at room temperature.
NUTRITIONAL VALUE: As grapefruit.
INDUSTRIAL PROCESSING: None.

126

Ugli
(Citrus sp.)

DESCRIPTION: A large, more or less spherical citrus fruit, up to 6¼in (16cm) in diameter, with a very knobbly, yellowish-green or yellowish-brown, thick skin loosely attached to the flesh. The segments are easy to remove and separate, and contain few pips. The flesh is very juicy, generally sweet and rather fragrant.

COUNTRY OF ORIGIN: Jamaica.

PRODUCER COUNTRIES: Jamaica, some South American countries.

AVAILABILITY: February to June.

USE: Peel and eat fresh or cut and scoop out segments.

KEEPING QUALITIES: About one week at room temperature.

NUTRITIONAL VALUE: Not known.

INDUSTRIAL PROCESSING: None.

Sambal
(Citrus amblycarpa)

DESCRIPTION: Small, bright green citrus fruit, ½-1½in (15-35mm) in diameter, with a dull, gnarled and lumpy skin that changes to pale green on ripening. The flesh is dark green, very fragrant, but also very tart.

COUNTRIES OF ORIGIN: Indonesia.

PRODUCER COUNTRIES: Indonesia, Thailand.

AVAILABILITY: Throughout the year, but irregular.

USE: Use the juice as lemon juice. Also used in traditional Indonesian cooking.

KEEPING QUALITIES: A few weeks at room temperature.

NUTRITIONAL VALUE: Not known.

△ Sambal, 2in (50mm) diameter   ▽ Lime, 2in (46mm) diameter

Lime
(Citrus aurantiifolia)

DESCRIPTION: Round or ovoid fruit, ½-2in (2-5cm) long, green or greenish-yellow in colour. The flesh is bright green and more acid and fragrant than that of the lemon. There are various varieties but they are seldom sold by name.

COUNTRIES OF ORIGIN: Malaysia.

PRODUCER COUNTRIES: Most tropical countries where citrus fruits flourish.

AVAILABILITY: Throughout the year from various producing countries.

USE: As lemon.

KEEPING QUALITIES: About ten days at room temperature.

NUTRITIONAL VALUE: As lemon.

INDUSTRIAL PROCESSING: Lemonade, juice, jam, pickle; oil from the skin is used in the perfume industry.

Seville Orange
(Citrus aurantium)

DESCRIPTION: A rather small, round orange with thick, dull orange-yellow skin, and not particularly attractive. The flesh contains a lot less juice than other oranges. Has a characteristically bitter taste which makes very piquant marmalade.

COUNTRY OF ORIGIN: Tropical Asia.

PRODUCER COUNTRIES: Spain, Italy.

AVAILABILITY: November to July.

USE: Not suitable for eating fresh; peel and flesh used for making Seville marmalade.

KEEPING QUALITIES: Several weeks.

NUTRITIONAL VALUE: Not known.

INDUSTRIAL PROCESSING: Candied peel, marmalade, liqueurs such as Cointreau and Grand Marnier.

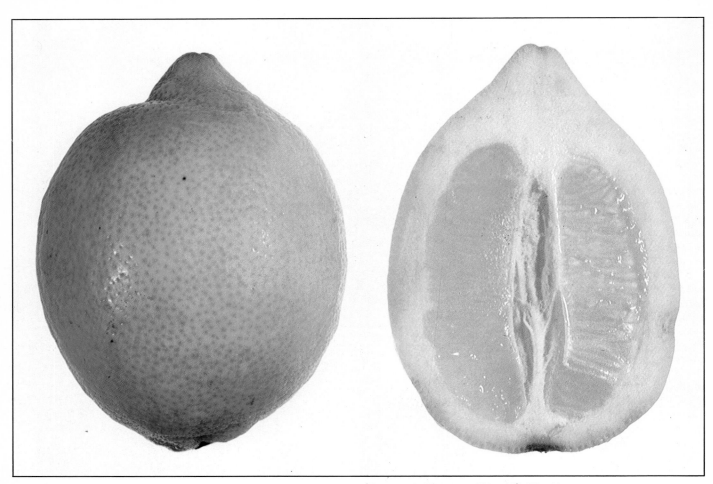

△ Hermosa, 4in (96mm) long ▽ Limoni, 2½in (68mm) long

Bergamot
(Citrus bergamia)
DESCRIPTION: Looks like a small, round, greenish-yellow lemon. Has very oily, fragrant skin and inedible, very acid flesh.

COUNTRY OF ORIGIN: Italy.

PRODUCER COUNTRY: Italy.

AVAILABILITY: Throughout the year, though irregular.

USE: Virtually none except in the Italian speciality *mostarde di frutta* (peeled and candied in mustard syrup).

KEEPING QUALITIES: About two weeks.

NUTRITIONAL VALUE: Not known.

INDUSTRIAL PROCESSING: Essential oil from skin used in eau de cologne.

Shaddock
(Citrus grandis maxima)
DESCRIPTION: Large fruits weighing up to 11lb (5kg). Can be up to 8in (20cm) in diameter. There are both round and pear-shaped varieties. The yellow or sometimes pink-tinted skin surrounds the flesh very loosely and is quite thick. The segments inside are greenish-yellow to red, and contain a number of large, yellowish-white pips. The taste is spicy-sweet.

COUNTRIES OF ORIGIN: Asia.

PRODUCER COUNTRIES: Thailand, Malaysia, Indonesia.

AVAILABILITY: Throughout the year.

USE: Peel and eat fresh, or make into jam or jelly; the peel can be candied.

KEEPING QUALITIES: About two weeks at room temperature.

NUTRITIONAL VALUE: Not known.

INDUSTRIAL PROCESSING: Jam, fruit syrup.

△ Calamansi, 1in (27mm) diameter

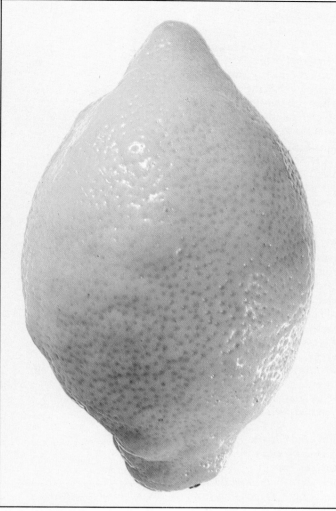

△ Verna, 5in (129mm) long

Lemon
(Citrus limonia)

DESCRIPTION: A round or elongated fruit, sometimes tapering to a point at one or both ends, and up to 5in (13cm) long. Skin fairly thick and pale to deep yellow in colour. The flesh is juicy and acid, and divided into segments that contain varying numbers of pips. The different varieties are not sold under their own names.

COUNTRIES OF ORIGIN: Southeast Asia.

PRODUCER COUNTRIES: All citrus-producing countries.

AVAILABILITY: Throughout the year.

USE: Squeeze the juice for culinary use (to acidulate cooking water, set jam, in dressings and marinades) or as a refreshing summer drink with sugar and water.

STORAGE: Several weeks; lemons dry out if kept too long.

NUTRITIONAL VALUE: 28 Kcal, 10 i.u. vitamin A and 37mg vitamin C per 100g serving.

INDUSTRIAL PROCESSING: Fruit drinks, juice concentrate, candied peel, flavourings, distilled.

Varieties

Eureka An American variety, only exported to Europe if European producer countries are unable to meet local demand. An egg-shaped or elongated variety with a smooth, bright yellow skin and few, if any, pips. Very piquant and fragrant.

Femminello An almost round lemon with a 'nose' at one end. The flesh is greenish-yellow, aromatic and contains few pips. Available throughout the year.

Hermosa An elongated, deep yellow lemon from Spain, with a small 'nose'. On the market from May to October. The light yellow flesh is full-flavoured, strongly scented, and contains few, if any, pips.

Limoni Not really a variety in its own right but the second crop of 'Primofiori' (q.v.). Somewhat smaller than the first crop, and on sale from December to May.

Lisbon A variety of Portuguese origin, grown mainly in the United States. Round to oval, with a pronounced 'nose', and dark yellow skin. The juicy flesh is has a very pungent smell.

Primofiori A variety grown in Italy and Spain, and harvested early. Generally ovoid, yellow, sometimes with a trace of green, and very juicy. Available September to April.

Speciale or **Speciali** Bright yellow, elongated lemon with a pronounced 'nose'. The skin is remarkably thin for a lemon and the flesh contains twice as much juice as other varieties. Available from September to December.

Verna A variety tapering at both ends, deep yellow in colour, and mainly grown in Spain. The flesh is seedless and juicy and comparatively sweet. Available between February and August.

Citron
(Citrus medica)

DESCRIPTION: Large, yellow fruits, 4-8in (10-20cm) long, weighing 1½-4lb (700-1500g), with very thick, pithy skin. Less juicy than the average lemon but sweeter. Has a scent which reminds one of cedarwood, which is why it is also called the cedarlemon.
COUNTRIES OF ORIGIN: Southeast Asia.
PRODUCER COUNTRIES: Italy, Greece, India, United States.
AVAILABILITY: Throughout the year, but irregular.
USE: Not eaten fresh, but used to make candied peel (halve the fruit, remove the flesh, steep the peel in salted water for at least a month, then wash and boil in a solution of water and sugar).
KEEPING QUALITIES: Several weeks.
NUTRITIONAL VALUE: Not known.
INDUSTRIAL PROCESSING: Candied peel.

Fingered Citron
(Citrus medica var. sarcodactylus)

DESCRIPTION: A longish fruit with finger-shaped outgrowths which sometimes fuse together; there is virtually no flesh in these appendages. The smell is very strong. A relative of the citron.
COUNTRIES OF ORIGIN: Asia.
PRODUCER COUNTRIES: Southeast Asia, Italy.
AVAILABILITY: June to September, but sporadic.
USE: In Asia the fruit is stuck with cloves and placed among clothing and bed linen to keep insects away.
KEEPING QUALITIES: Not known.
NUTRITIONAL VALUE: Not known.
INDUSTRIAL PROCESSING: Candied peel; oil from the skin is used in perfume.

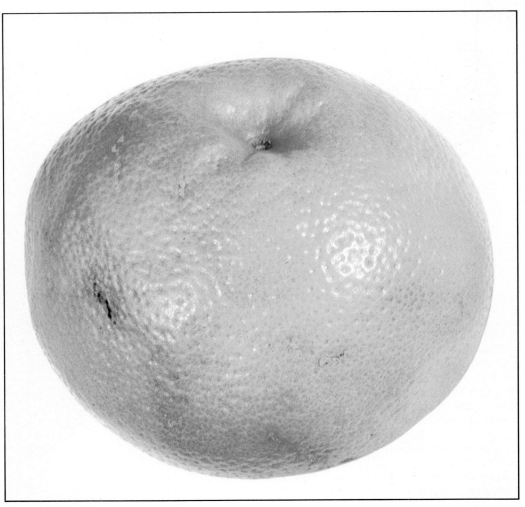

△ Royal, 5in (130mm) diameter

Calamansi
(Citrus microcarpa)

DESCRIPTION: Small, round citrus fruit, 1-1¼in (2-3cm) in diameter and greenish-yellow to orange in colour. Also called *calamundin* or *mundu*. The flesh, which contains many pips, is deep orange in colour, very sweet and perfumed.
COUNTRIES OF ORIGIN: Southeast Asia.
PRODUCER COUNTRIES: Indonesia, Thailand.
AVAILABILITY: Throughout the year, but sporadic.
USE: As lime.
KEEPING QUALITIES: About ten days at room temperature.
NUTRITIONAL VALUE: Not known.
INDUSTRIAL PROCESSING: None.

Grapefruit
(Citrus paradisi)

DESCRIPTION: Round or slightly flattened fruit, up to 6in (15cm) in diameter, with pale yellow to orange-red skin, depending on the variety. The thickness of the skin varies, and may or may not be easy to remove — again it depends on the variety. The flesh is pale yellow or, in the the 'pink' varieties, palest pink to blood red; the redder the colour the sweeter the taste. The flesh is divided into segments that are easy to separate in some varieties and difficult to separate in others. Some varieties have pips, others do not.
COUNTRIES OF ORIGIN: Southeast Asia.
PRODUCER COUNTRIES: Spain, Israel, Cyprus, Egypt, South Africa, United States, Central America.
AVAILABILITY: Throughout the year from various producer countries.
USE: Peel and eat like an orange, or halve the fruit and scoop the flesh out of the segments. Add peel and flesh to marmalade, or squeeze for juice.
KEEPING QUALITIES: Two weeks at room temperature.
NUTRITIONAL VALUE: 40 Kcal, 80 i.u. vitamin A and 40mg vitamin C per 100g serving.
INDUSTRIAL PROCESSING: Juice, canned syrup.

Varieties

Duncan This is the oldest American grapefruit variety, and the ancestor of the whole grapefruit tribe. It is a slightly flattened, smallish fruit, with a rather thick, yellow skin and yellow flesh. In taste and smell 'Duncan' is still without peer among yellow grapefruit. Available throughout the year.

△ Ruby Red, 4in (96mm) diameter   ▽ Marsh Seedless, 4in (100mm) diameter

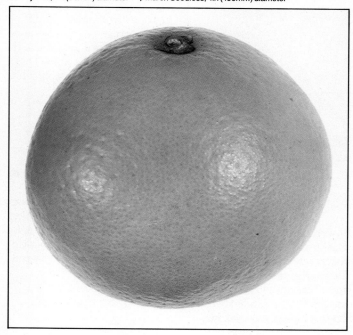

Foster The oldest of the pink-fleshed varieties, but probably nearing the end of its commercial career due to the development of better pink and red varieties. Supplies are available from November to March from older plantations in Mediterranean producing countries.

Marsh Seedless A pale yellow, spherical or slightly flattened grapefruit that sometimes turns darker yellow when fully ripe. The yellow flesh is juicy, has only a faint aroma and contains no pips; the 12-14 segments have very thin membranes. An exceptionally good variety to eat fresh for breakfast or as an appetizer. Grown in all citrus-producing countries and on the market throughout the year.

Royal A variety grown in southern Italy, Cyprus and Eygpt from November to March. 'Royal' can stay on the tree for a long time without spoiling; the longer it is left to ripen, the deeper yellow the skin and flesh; eventually both turn pink. The riper the fruit, the sweeter the taste. Has a rather thick skin, but is easy to peel.

Ruby or **Ruby Red** A natural mutation of 'Thompson' (q.v.), discovered in 1929 at a fruit research station in Texas. Most supplies still come from Texas, although the variety is also grown elsewhere. A round or flattish round grapefruit with deep yellow or yellowish-pink skin. The flesh is pink, very sweet and juicy, and smells good. There are no pips. On the market throughout the year.

Star Ruby This variety, grown commercially since 1970, was developed in the United States. Spherical, sometimes slightly flattened, with a yellow or orange-red skin which peels easily. The flesh is blood-red, very sweet and very firm. The segments separate easily, hence its popularity as a dessert variety. Often sold under the trade name Sunrise . Exported from United States throughout the year, especially between September and April.

Thompson Also known as 'Pink Marsh'. A natural mutation of 'Marsh Seedless', but sweeter-tasting and with a deep yellow skin that sometimes has a single red spot. Available throughout the year.

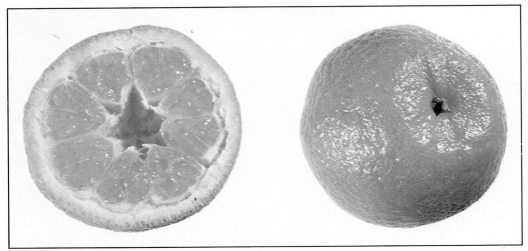

△ Clementine, 2½in (64mm) diameter ▽ Kara, 3in (71mm) diameter

Mandarin
(Citrus reticulata)
DESCRIPTION: Round or slightly flattened fruit, up to 4½in (12cm) in diameter, depending on variety, and ranging in colour from yellowish-green to orange-red. The flesh can also vary in colour; it is generally sweet to very sweet, characteristically pungent, and the number of pips varies from none to many. Most varieties are easy to peel because the skin is fairly loose around the segments inside. Frequently crossed with other citrus species (see page 124).
COUNTRIES OF ORIGIN: China, Japan, Philippines.
PRODUCER COUNTRIES: All citrus-producing countries, but especially Spain, Italy, Morocco, Algeria, Israel, South Africa, United States.

AVAILABILITY: Throughout the year; peak months October to March.
USE: Peel and eat fresh; use as cake decoration, or in ice-cream, in fruit salads, added to other citrus fruits in jams and marmalades, or bottled in syrup.
KEEPING QUALITIES: About ten days at room temperature.
NUTRITIONAL VALUE: 46 Kcal, 420 i.u. vitamin A and 31mg vitamin C per 100g serving.
INDUSTRIAL PROCESSING: Canned in syrup, jam, juice.

Varieties

Bowen A cross between the 'Dancy' tangerine (which it closely resembles) and the 'Duncan' grapefruit; such crosses are known as 'tangelos', especially in the United States. Shape is plump and oval. Has an orange skin and tasty, orange-yellow flesh. Available between October and January.

Clauselina An early Spanish variety, on the market from early November. Probably a cross between 'Satsuma' and 'Clementine'. The fruits are flattish and pale orange. The flesh is deliciously juicy.

Clementine An accidental cross discovered in 1902 in Algeria in the garden of Father Pierre Clément (hence its name). This very popular mandarin-type orange is usually, but not always, flattish and deep orange in colour. Generally seedless, juicy and sweet. The segments are only loosely attached to each other and the peel comes away easily. Exported mainly from Spain, Italy, Morocco and Algeria. Available November to February.

Dancy An American tangerine, grown in United States, Israel and South Africa, and available January to May and October to December. An easy peeler, deep orange or orange-red skin, and deep orange flesh. Juicy and sweet, and contains 3-10 pips.

Kara This is an improved 'King' (q.v.), obtained from a cross with 'Satsuma'. Thanks to crossbreeding the number of pips has been reduced and the variety is robust enough to grow in sub-tropical regions. Mainly exported from Spain in March and April. Flattish, and orange-yellow in colour. The orange flesh is reasonably juicy.

King This variety is a cross between 'Satsuma' and an unknown orange variety — such crosses are known as 'tangors'. Grows especially well in places with a very warm climate, such as Florida and Arizona, Africa and Australia. Flattish fruits, yellowish-green to orange. Flesh is pale orange and tangy sweet, and contains lots of pips. Available between May and September.

△ Murcott, 3in (74mm) diameter

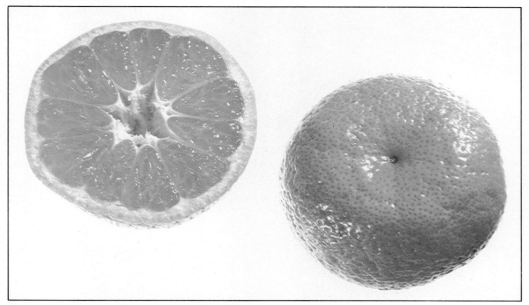

△ Satsuma, 3¼in (78mm) diameter   ▽Minneola, 3¼in (82mₙn) diameter

Murcott Also called 'Honey Tangerine' or 'Murcott Honey Orange'. A cross between a tangerine and an orange. First appeared on the market in 1958. Grown mainly in United States, and exported between December and April. A flattish fruit, deep orange in colour. The juicy, orange flesh contains up to 20 pips.

Orlando and **Minneola** Two virtually identical crosses between a tangerine and a grapefruit (hence the name 'tangelo'). Both varieties taper to a 'nose' at the stalk end. Skin is deep orange. Flesh is sweet, mouthwateringly juicy, with a tangy fragrance. Few pips. Exported from United States, Israel and South Africa January to May and September to December.

Satsuma A mandarin of Japanese origin, named after the province where it was produced. Now also grown in Spain and Israel. An early variety, flattish, and with a light orange skin. The flesh still has a hint of tartness when it arrives in the shops. Few, if any, pips. 'Owari' is another mandarin variety. Available between October and January.

Tambor A cross between a tangerine and a South African orange. The fruits are very large, rather flattened, and often have a navel. The colour is deep orange; the sweet, juicy flesh contains few, if any, pips. Available in July and August.

Mikan A tangerine variety with small, sweet fruits that are rarely sold for eating fresh; almost 90 per cent of the 'Mikan' crop — from Spain, Japan and Taiwan — goes for canning. If exported fresh, 'Mikans' appear on the market from January to March.

△ Temple, 4¼in (102mm) diameter   ▽ Topaz, 3¼in (81mm) diameter

Temple Also called 'King Orange', 'Temple' is a hybrid of uncertain parentage; probably a descendant of the mandarin and the orange. Fruits are large, slightly pear-shaped, and have a deep orange, rather wrinkly skin. The flesh is juicy and tangy, and contains a lot of large pips. Exported between January and May from various citrus-growing countries.

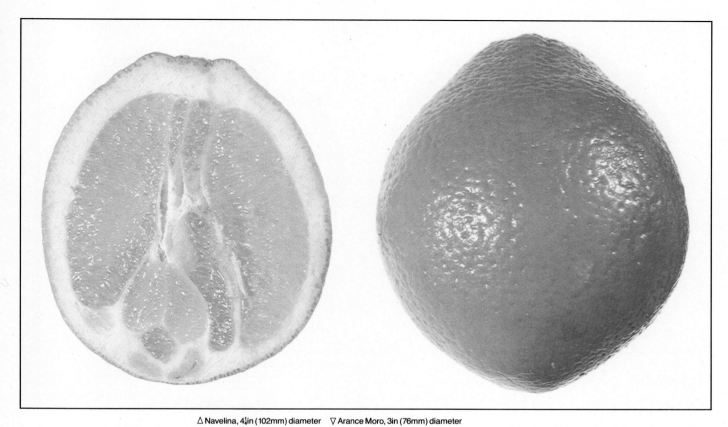

△ Navelina, 4¼in (102mm) diameter ▽ Arance Moro, 3in (76mm) diameter

Topaz An easy-to-peel cross between an orange and a tangerine, light orange in colour, with sweet, fragrant, orange-coloured flesh with few pips. Exported in April and May, almost exclusively from Israel, where the variety first appeared. Often sold under the trademark Jaffarine, though this is used for other citrus varieties too.

Tardivi A true mandarin, also known as 'Mandarine', 'Ciaculli' and 'Tardivo de Ciaculli'. Originally from Indo-China and now mainly grown in Italy, especially Sicily. The skin is light orange in colour. The orange flesh contains many pips, is sweet and juicy and gives off a strong smell when peeled. Available between January and April.

Orange
(Citrus sinensis)

DESCRIPTION: Round or oval fruit, up to 6in (15cm) across, with a leathery skin that varies in thickness and contains a great deal of oil. Depending on the variety, the skin may be green, greenish-yellow, orange and even red (blood oranges). Some varieties (navels) develop a fruit-within-a-fruit at the opposite end to the stalk. Some species have pips, others not. The soft, juicy, flesh is yellow, orange or red in colour and is divided into segments. The taste ranges from sharp and acid to very sweet.

COUNTRIES OF ORIGIN: China, Japan.

PRODUCER COUNTRIES: Virtually all countries between latitudes 40° North and 40° South.

AVAILABILITY: Throughout the year from various producer countries.

USE: Peel and eat fresh; squeeze for juice; use peel, juice and flesh for marmalade; candy peel; use in desserts and fruit salads; bottle in sugar syrup or alcohol; slice and candy; use as garnish for meat, fish and poultry.

KEEPING QUALITIES: A few weeks; longer in the refrigerator.

NUTRITIONAL VALUE: 40 Kcal, 200 i.u. vitamin A and 50mg vitamin C per 100g serving.

INDUSTRIAL PROCESSING: Juice, concentrates, marmalade, canned in syrup, candied, flavourings, distilled into liqueur.

135

Varieties

Arance Moro or **Moro** A blood orange — blood oranges appeared in the Mediterranean area around 1850. Two types of blood orange are grown today: full blood oranges (q.v.), which have red skin and red flesh, and semi-blood oranges in which only the flesh is red. 'Arance Moro' is the earliest semi-blood variety, on the market from November to February and exported from Italy, Spain, Cyprus and Morocco. It is quite a small orange with a rough, thick, deep orange skin and red-speckled flesh which tastes wonderfully sweet. Equally suitable for eating fresh and making juice.

Blood Oval A full blood orange, oval in shape, also known as 'Oval Sanguina'. The smooth skin is speckled with red, as is the flesh, which contains few pips. The flavour is full and sweet. Exported from January to March, mainly from Italy and North Africa.

Cadanera A spherical, sometimes slightly oval, Spanish variety, with deep orange skin and sweet, juicy flesh. Contains 10-11 segments. Exported between November and March. An outstanding eating orange.

Griolla Originally an Italian variety, but now cultivated mainly in South America (Cuba, Surinam) and mostly sold for making juice. Sweet and very juicy despite its rather fibrous flesh. The skin is yellowish-green, changing to orange-brown as the fruit ripens. Exported throughout the year.

Hamlin A variety produced in the United States. More or less spherical, with very thin, orange-yellow skin and very juicy, yellow flesh virtually devoid of pips. The taste is very perfumed. Exported from South America and South Africa February to March, and from Morocco and United States July to December.

Macetera One of the finest Spanish varieties, but not often available. A more or less spherical orange with 10 segments and usually no pips. The skin is thin and light orange in colour, and the flesh is honey-sweet and very juicy. Available February to April.

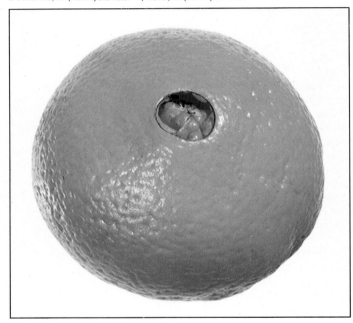

Navel or **Washington Navel** A spherical fruit with a large navel, orange-red skin and very sweet flesh divided into 9-11 segments. This variety is grown in North and South America, South Africa and Australia, as well as various Mediterranean countries. Available between November and January. A good eating orange.

△ Trovita (left), 3¼in (83mm) diameter   Griolla (middle), 3in (72mm) diameter   Shamouti Sharon (right), 2¾in (67mm) diameter

Navelina An early navel orange, exported between October and mid-November from Spain, South Africa and United States. It is a natural mutation of 'Washington Navel' (see above), a longish, pale orange fruit with a pronounced navel and flesh that tends to be tart at the beginning of the harvesting season, getting sweeter towards the end of it. A good eating variety.

Navellate Another close relative of 'Washington Navel' (see above), but comes on the market later (January to May). It is smaller and rounder than 'Navel', pipless and has an almost closed navel. The flesh is fairly sweet and very juicy.

Pera A close relative of 'Shamouti' (q.v.), specially bred for the tropics. Mainly grown in Brazil and suitable both for eating fresh and for making into juice. Ripe fruits are reddish-orange, and more or less spherical. The flesh is sweet and very juicy. Available between May and October.

Salustiana An extremely popular variety, exported mainly from Spain and Morocco between November and April. The fruits are slightly flattened. The skin is light orange, and the flesh is deep orange, deliciously sweet and contains few pips. There are usually 10-12 segments. Suitable both for eating fresh and making into juice.

Sanguina Redonda or **Round Sanguina** A semi-blood orange (see 'Arance Moro'), slightly flattened, with a deep orange skin with red speckling. The flesh is also deep orange, delightfully sweet, and very fragrant. Contains 10-12 segments and very few pips. Exported between January and April from Italy, Spain and Morocco.

Shamouti An Italian variety derived from 'Belladi', a variety grown in Egypt and Lebanon. Oval fruits, with an orange-yellow skin noticeably thicker at the stalk end. Fairly easy to peel. The flesh is yellow and sweet, but not especially juicy. Improved 'Shamouti' varieties are 'Shamouti Hadel' and 'Shamouti Sharon'. Grown in Israel, Greece, Egypt, Cyprus and Tunisia. Often exported from Israel as 'Jaffa' oranges, although 'Jaffa' is also the trade mark for other varieties. Available December to April.

Tarocco A full blood orange with orange-red skin and flesh. Quite large fruits with a pronounced bulge at the stalk end. The flesh is divided into 9-11 segments, and is honey-sweet, juicy and very fragrant. Available, mainly from Italy, between January and April.

Tomango A South African variety, on the market between May and August (under the brand name 'Outspan') and an exceptionally good table fruit. Large and round, with a deep orange skin and yellow-orange flesh. The flesh is tender, sweet and juicy.

Trovita Mainly grown in Greece and Israel, but also becoming popular with growers in South Africa. Round or oval fruit, deep orange in colour, and with sweet, juicy flesh, divided into 9-12 segments. Available from Greece and Israel between November and January, and between May and July from South Africa.

Valencia or **Valencia Late** The world's most important variety of orange, well established in all countries that grow citrus fruits. A round or slightly oval orange, not very large, and divided into 8-13 segments, usually containing no pips. The skin is fairly smooth and yellowish-orange; the thin membranes around the segments are soft and easily digestible. The flesh is deliciously sweet and juicy. 'Valencia' is suitable both for making juice and eating fresh. When grown in the tropics, skin colour may be green to brownish-yellow, and the flesh rather more fibrous; these fruits are more suitable for pressing. Available throughout the year.

Verna A late orange from Spain, Italy and North Africa, also called 'Berna' or 'Bednar' and available between March and July. The fruits are relatively small, round or slightly oval, and orange-yellow in colour. The flesh tends to be somewhat fibrous, though pleasantly sharp; more suitable for making juice than for eating fresh.

Kumquat
(Fortunella ssp.)
DESCRIPTION: A thumb-sized citrus fruit, 1-1½in (2-4cm) long, usually bright orange in colour. The edible skin is quite thin; the flesh inside is light orange, divided into a number of segments, and usually contains a lot of pale green pips. The flavour is pleasantly sharp and fragrant.
COUNTRY OF ORIGIN: China.
PRODUCER COUNTRIES: France, Italy, Spain, South Africa, Brazil.
AVAILABILITY: Throughout the year from various producer countries.

USE: Eat fresh (with skin); make into compote, bottle in syrup or brandy, make into marmalade, or use in fruit salads; serve in thin slices in cocktails, or prick whole fruits with a sharp fork and allow cocktail to absorb the tangy flavour.
KEEPING QUALITIES: About one week at room temperature.
NUTRITIONAL VALUE: Not known.
INDUSTRIAL PROCESSING: Jam, marmalade, canned in syrup.

Sapindaceae

Akee, lungan, lychee, rambutan, pulasan, quenette

The *Sapindaceae* family comprises some 1,000 species, most of which grow in the tropics. They vary greatly in form — some are trees, some are bushes and some are climbing plants with tendrils like watch springs which coil firmly around their support. The family owes its name to the genus *Sapindus,* which in turn owes its name to the presence of saponins, soapy alkaline substances, in its fruits. Like soap, naturally occurring saponins are good cleansing agents and can be used to wash clothes and hair and even remove stubborn stains. There are 15 species in the genus *Sapindus,* all of them indigenous to the tropics. Many saponins are poisonous — in some areas they are used to stun or kill fish.

Only one edible fruit is partly poisonous and that is the akee. This is West African in origin, but now grows in Central and South America as well. It is the pink-coloured membrane between the pip and the flesh which is poisonous, sometimes fatally so; in Jamaica akee poisoning occasionally causes 'vomiting sickness', once incorrectly diagnosed as 'brain infection'. The genus name *Blighia* preserves for posterity the name of Captain Bligh of the *Bounty,* who was carrying specimens of the akee plant from the South Pacific to the West Indies at the time of the notorious mutiny.

All other edible fruits of the *Sapindaceae* family are entirely innocuous. Some are especially prized, particularly the lychee, originally from China but now grown commercially in other tropical and sub-tropical countries. Although lychees have been sold in canned form in the West for many years, freshly imported lychees are a fairly recent phenomenon. Only fresh fruits have the characteristic lychee perfume; this all but disappears when the fruit is canned.

Apart from the lychee and occasionally the rambutan, the rest of the edible *Sapindaceae* are very rarely seen in the West. However, if growers succeed in improving quality and consistency, this may change.

△ Lungan, 1½in (35mm) diameter

Akee
(Blighia sapida)
DESCRIPTION: An elongated, three-sided fruit resembling a small paprika. The colour is scarlet. Ripe fruits burst open, exposing the juicy flesh which contains a large, brown pip the size of a marble. Between the pip and the flesh there is a pink membrane which is poisonous.
COUNTRIES OF ORIGIN: West Africa.
PRODUCER COUNTRIES: West Africa, Brazil, Jamaica.
AVAILABILITY: October to May but very irregular.
USE: Peel, remove pip and membrane; eat flesh on its own or use in fruit salads, ice-cream, etc.
KEEPING QUALITIES: One to two days at room temperature.
OTHER INFORMATION: Not known.

Lungan or **Longyen** or **Dragon's Eye**
(Euphoria longana)
DESCRIPTION: Roundish fruits, 1-1½in (3-4cm) in diameter with an orange skin that turns beige-brown within 24 hours of picking. The skin is generally smooth (though sometimes covered with a woolly fuzz like a peach) but quickly hardens. Even when hard, it is easy to remove. The flesh is juicy and tasty.
COUNTRIES OF ORIGIN: Southeast Asia.
PRODUCER COUNTRIES: India.
AVAILABILITY: December to May.
USE: As lychee.
KEEPING QUALITIES: One to two days at room temperature.
NUTRITIONAL VALUE: Not known; probably as lychee.
INDUSTRIAL PROCESSING: Canned in syrup, liqueur.

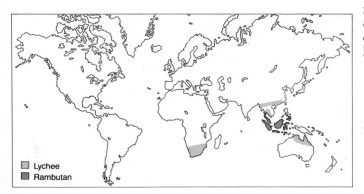

☐ Lychee
☐ Rambutan

△ Rambutan, 2in (48mm) long   ▽ Lychee, 1½in (38mm) long

Lychee
(Litchi chinensis)

DESCRIPTION: Round fruits 1-2in (3-5cm) in diameter. Grow in trusses of up to 30 but usually sold loose. Lychees have a deep pink to brownish-yellow skin. This hardens after a few days but is easy to remove. The flesh is white or yellowish-white in colour, slightly translucent, sweet, juicy, and delicately perfumed. The longish pip is brown and can be eaten roasted.
COUNTRY OF ORIGIN: China.
PRODUCER COUNTRIES: Israel, South Africa, Thailand, China.
AVAILABILITY: November to March and July to August from various producer countries.
USE: Peel and eat fresh or use in desserts, ice-cream, etc.

KEEPING QUALITIES: About one week at room temperature.
NUTRITIONAL VALUE: 64 Kcal and 42g vitamin C per 100g serving.
INDUSTRIAL PROCESSING: Canned in syrup, dried.

Rambutan
(Nephelium lappaceum)

DESCRIPTION: Red or brownish-yellow fruits that grow in trusses and are often sold that way too. Rambutans are 1½-3in (4-8cm) in diameter and rather untidy in appearance because covered with long, soft spines or hairs. The flesh (actually the seed coat) is pale yellow, translucent, juicy, sweet, and pleasantly scented, but on the whole less tasty than that of the lychee. 'Rambutan' comes from the Malay word rambut, meaning 'hair'.
COUNTRIES OF ORIGIN: Malaysia, Indonesia.
PRODUCER COUNTRIES: Thailand, Indonesia, Malaysia.
AVAILABILITY: Throughout the year.
USE: Peel with your fingers and eat the flesh fresh, or use in fruit salads or desserts.
KEEPING QUALITIES: At least one week at room temperature.
NUTRITIONAL VALUE: As lychee.
INDUSTRIAL PROCESSING: Canned in syrup.

Pulasan
(Nephelium mutabile)

DESCRIPTION: Related to, and indeed similar to, the lychee. The fruits are violet-red and covered with short, warty spines. The sweet, juicy flesh comes away from the skin quite easily. More strongly scented than the rambutan. The seeds can be eaten roasted.
COUNTRY OF ORIGIN: Philippines.
PRODUCER COUNTRIES: Indonesia, Philippines.
AVAILABILITY: September to May.
USE: As lychee.
KEEPING QUALITIES: One week at room temperature.
NUTRITIONAL VALUE: As lychee.
INDUSTRIAL PROCESSING: Canned in syrup.

Quenette or Honey Berry
(Melicocca bijuga)

DESCRIPTION: Large, round fruits approximately 1½in (4cm) across. The thin skin is green and leathery; the flesh is yellowish-white, soft and juicy, varying in taste from very tart to honey-sweet. There is a large brown stone.
COUNTRIES OF ORIGIN: Tropical America and Caribbean.
PRODUCER COUNTRIES: Caribbean, northern South America.
AVAILABILITY: Throughout the year, but peaking between October and May.
USE: Peel and eat ripe fruits fresh or use in fruit salads, ice-cream etc; tart or unripe fruits can be made into chutney, jam, etc.
KEEPING QUALITIES: One week at room temperature.
NUTRITIONAL VALUE: Not known.
INDUSTRIAL PROCESSING: Canned in syrup.

Sapotaceae
Sapodilla

The *Sapotaceae* family comprises some 600 species, some of which bear edible fruits. Most of these, however, scarcely figure in the international fruit trade. Great confusion reigns about which fruits belong to which species. Though South American in origin, most species have been cultivated in many different tropical countries since the 16th century. This has led not only to a profusion of colloquial names, but also to considerable variations in shape, colour, taste, sugar content, and so on, and because these fruits have no great economic significance no one has felt the need to create order out of the chaos. The *Sapotaceae* are indigenous to Central and South America, or more specifically to countries from southern Mexico to northern Brazil.

All members of the *Sapotaceae* have one thing in common: when damaged they exude a rubbery latex. The latex of one particular species is used in the manufacture of chewing gum; the latex of another is used to manufacture a non-elastic, rubbery product called guttapercha, traditionally used to insulate underwater telegraph cables.

The best known fruit-bearing species in this family is *Achras sapota*, known as the sapodilla in Central and South America, but elsewhere as sapote, sawo and kauki. The sawo and kauki, which come from Southeast Asia, have been given scientific names in their own right *(Mimusops sapote* and *Mimusops kauki)*, and differ considerably in shape, colour and taste from their South American parent. The general opinion among experts, however, is that the sapodilla, sapote, sawo and kauki are essentially the same fruit. The specimens that occasionally reach us in the West are mainly exported from Thailand and Indonesia.

Several other *Sapotaceae* fruits put in an occasional appearance at major fruit exhibitions where exporters and importers are keen to attract attention with unusual products. But here again confusion reigns: the Mamey or Mamey sapote is often confused with the San Domingo apricot which belongs to the *Guttiferae* family, and the casimiroa or white sapote *(Casimirea edulis)* does not belong to the *Sapotaceae* family at all but to the *Rutaceae* (see page 125).

△ Sapodilla, 3in (71mm) long

Sapodilla
(Achras sapote)

DESCRIPTION: Round or oval fruit, 1¼-3in (3-8cm) long, with a thin, brown skin rather like that of a potato. Southeast Asian fruits are dark orange in colour. The flesh has the consistency of an apple; it is light brown, sometimes with a reddish tinge and has a core containing as many as 12 shiny black pips up to ¾in (2cm) long, though sometimes there are no pips at all. Ripe fruits taste sweet, unripe fruits taste sour. The smell is a combination of pear, apricot and honey.

COUNTRIES OF ORIGIN: Central and South America.

PRODUCER COUNTRIES: Thailand, Indonesia, Malaysia, Mexico, Philippines, Venezuela.

AVAILABILITY: Throughout the year, but irregular.

USE: Cut in half and scoop out flesh; eat ripe fruits fresh, and make unripe fruits into jam.

KEEPING QUALITIES: Ripe fruits: a few days at room temperature.

NUTRITIONAL VALUE: 60 i.u. vitamin A and 14mg vitamin C per 100g serving.

INDUSTRIAL PROCESSING: None.

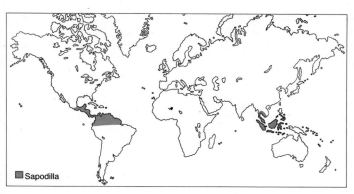

Sapodilla

Saxifragales
Gooseberry, blackcurrant, redcurrant, white currant

Experts vigorously disagree as to the proper place of the genus *Ribes* within the plant kingdom. Some include the 140 or so *Ribes* species in the *Saxifragaceae* family, others regard them as a separate family within the larger *Saxifragales* group, and others declare them to be a family in their own right and call them the *Ribesiaceae* or *Grossulariaceae*.

Most *Ribes* species are indigenous to the temperate zones of the northern hemisphere, but a few occur in the mountains of Central and South America. The few fruit-bearing varieties — currant, blackcurrant and gooseberry — are almost exclusively cultivated north of the Equator, predominantly in Western and Eastern Europe.

Although the three species mentioned all occur in the wild, they do not seem to have been cultivated until relatively recently. The Greeks and Romans did not seem to know them; the first records date from the 15th century. The gooseberry is the exception; it was described by the Arabs, conquerors of Spain in the 8th century. In the Middle East, the Arabs cultivated a kind of rhubarb they called *ribas* and used it as a medicinal plant. In Spain they used the wild gooseberry as a substitute for *ribas* because of its laxative effect, and so they called it *ribas* too. It is this confusion of names that probably gave rise to the genus name *Ribes*.

Today, far more gooseberries and currants are grown for processing than for selling fresh in the shops. The white currant — not a separate variety but a variant of the redcurrant — has become extremely rare indeed. Generally speaking, too, green gooseberries are now rarer in the shops than they were; most of them go straight to the cannery or jam-making factory. However, there have been determined efforts in recent years to develop larger, sweeter varieties for eating; these tend to be amber, yellow, or pinkish in colour.

The bulk of the blackcurrant harvest goes to the processing industry — as raw material for jams, fillings, soft drinks, syrups, and liqueurs (the French *cassis*, for example).

△ Achilles, 1¼in (31mm) diameter

American *Ribes* species are often grown in private gardens rather than commercially. Good examples are the black Worcesterberry and the bright red currant gooseberry, *R. divaricatum* and *R. hirtellum* respectively; these are not, as is often thought, crosses between the gooseberry and the blackcurrant, and between the gooseberry and the redcurrant, but species in their own right.

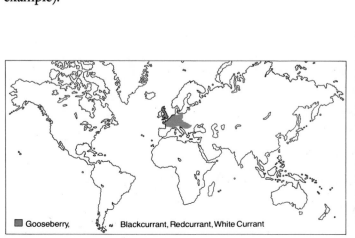

■ Gooseberry, ● Blackcurrant, Redcurrant, White Currant

Gooseberry
(Ribes grossularia)
DESCRIPTION: A green or red, sometimes slightly fuzzy berry, round or slightly oval and up to 1¼in (33mm) long. Can be eaten fresh if sweet, cooked if tart.
COUNTRIES OF ORIGIN: Western and Central Europe.
PRODUCER COUNTRIES: Germany, United Kingdom, Netherlands, Belgium, Poland, Czechoslovakia.

AVAILABILITY: June/July.
USE: Eat fresh, or stew with sugar, or use in fillings, jam, etc.
KEEPING QUALITIES: One to two days at room temperature; four to seven days in the refrigerator.
NUTRITIONAL VALUE: 30mg vitamin C per 100g serving.
INDUSTRIAL PROCESSING: Jam, canned in syrup.

Varieties

Achilles A large, oval gooseberry with a smooth, purplish-red skin which is soft and practically hairless. A good eating variety. Available second half of July.

Fredonia A very large late-cropping, dark red gooseberry grown in United States, but of English origin. Available July/August.

Poorman possibly the best quality American-type gooseberry. Has large red berries of excellent flavour and texture. Available July.

Whinham's Industry A variety of English origin. The rather large berries ripen to reddish-purple and are covered in short hairs. They taste and smell excellent. Available first half of July.

Whitesmith Also called 'English White'. Changes colour as it ripens from green to pale yellow. The skin is soft and hairless, the taste sweet and outstandingly fragrant. One of the nicest gooseberries for eating fresh but also suitable for processing. On the market late June and early July.

△ Whinham's Industry, 1 in (25mm) diameter   ▽ Whitesmith, 1 in (22mm) diameter

△ Blackcurrant, ½in (11mm) diameter   ▽ Fay's Prolific, ½in (11mm) diameter

Redcurrant
(Ribes sativum)

DESCRIPTION: Spherical berries approximately ½in (1cm) in diameter, growing in dense or straggly clusters. Translucent light to dark red. Flesh tart but sweetens on ripening, and contains yellowish-brown pips.

COUNTRIES OF ORIGIN: Europe, Western Asia.

PRODUCER COUNTRIES: Belgium, Netherlands, Germany, France, England, United Kingdom.

AVAILABILITY: From May onwards if grown under glass; mid-June to end August if grown in the open.

USE: Eat fresh (including skin and pips); use in fruit salads and desserts, or make into jam or jelly.

KEEPING QUALITIES: One to two days at room temperature; six days in the refrigerator.

NUTRITIONAL VALUE: 10mg vitamin C per 100g serving.

INDUSTRIAL PROCESSING: Jam, jelly, juice, soft drinks, syrup.

Varieties

Fay's Prolific An American cross developed towards the end of the last century and particularly suitable for growing under glass. This is why it is the earliest variety on sale. The quite large, firm, dark red berries grow in long clusters. The taste is slightly tart.

Jonkheer van Tets A Dutch cross from the 1930s, developed from 'Fay's Prolific' and an unknown variety. Has large, juicy berries that grow in longish clusters. Taste is slightly tart but faintly fragrant. On the market between mid-June and early July, and especially suitable for processing.

△ Rondom, ⅜in (11mm) diameter

△ Jonkheer van Tets, ½in (12mm) diameter

Rondom A firm berry that keeps relatively well in the refrigerator. A Dutch cross developed in 1934, and on the market since 1949. The berries are quite small, shiny, and grow in dense clusters. The taste is sharp. Because their fragrance is lost in processing, they are best eaten fresh. Available end July and early August.

Red Lake A large, light red redcurrant which grows in long clusters. The taste is sharp. Juicy, and therefore suitable both for processing and eating fresh. Available early July.

Stanza A late species with firm, darkish-red, relatively small small berries, growing in long clusters. Taste is rather sharp, with little aroma. Suitable for processing and for eating fresh.

Blackcurrant
(Ribes nigrum)
DESCRIPTION: Black, generally matt berries, intensely flavoured and at their sweetest when fully ripe. Grow in clusters, like redcurrants, but are generally sold loose. The bulk of the blackcurrant harvest goes for processing.
OTHER INFORMATION: See redcurrant.
NUTRITIONAL VALUE: 117mg vitamin C per 100g serving.
INDUSTRIAL PROCESSING: Juice, soft drinks, syrup, liqueur *(cassis)*.

Ben Lomond A mid-season (late July) variety of blackcurrant grown in United Kingdom and likely to replace 'Baldwin' as the standard variety. Not such a fine, intense flavour as 'Baldwin' but good for all types of processing, including juice. Flowers late and crops heavily.

△ Red Lake, ½in (12mm) diameter   ▽ White Currant, ½in (11mm) diameter

White Currant
(Ribes sativum)

DESCRIPTION: Creamy-coloured, translucent berries. The white currant is a variant of the redcurrant and differs little from it except in colour. The berries are just a little smaller and the taste is decidedly sweeter.

OTHER INFORMATION: See redcurrant.

INDUSTRIAL PROCESSING: None.

Solanaceae

Tree tomato, Cape gooseberry, Quito orange, peach tomato, melon pear, cannibal's tomato

The *Solanaceae* family, comprising about 1,800 species, is particularly well represented in tropical South America, but also occurs in many other parts of the world. Its members range from herbaceous plants, often of the climbing kind, to trees. Potatoes, tomatoes, aubergines and pimentos are all products of members of the *Solanaceae*. The family also contains many poisonous species. The berries and all the green parts of the potato, for example, are harmful, even if not deadly poisonous. Species such as henbane *(Hyoscyamus niger)*, thorn apple *(Datura stramonium)* and deadly nightshade *(Atropa belladonna)*, however, are all deadly poisonous. Many others cause sickness if inexpertly used, but if correctly prepared become useful drugs, stimulants (tobacco) or medicines.

None of the *Solanaceae* features largely in the international fruit trade, but a few species have market potential, either as dessert produce or for processing into juice. New Zealand growers have been experimenting extensively with the South American tree tomato or tamarillo, for example, in an attempt to match the commercial success of the kiwi fruit. Potential fruits for juice-making are the peach tomato or cocoña and especially the Quito orange (also known by the Spanish name *naranjilla*, meaning 'little orange'). The colour of its juice — an attractive green — could be a good selling point. Attempts have been made for several years, especially in Peru, to corner the world market for Quito orange juice and concentrate.

As with many types of fruit from the tropics, lack of money and know-how in potential producer countries is not conducive to the research needed to convert wild and semi-wild species into varieties that can compete on the world market. Even when commercial production has been established, the new fruit has to be efficiently distributed, and the consumers with the purchasing power wooed and won. Even the best export organizations are not always successful.

△ Tree Tomato, 2⅝in (66mm) long

Tree Tomato or **Tamarillo**
(Cyphomandra betacea)
DESCRIPTION: Oval fruits, 1½-2½in (4-7cm) long, tapering to a point at both ends, with a thin skin that ripens from orange-yellow to red or brownish-red, sometimes purple. Inside an envelope of firm flesh is a pulpy centre containing many small seeds. The skin tastes bitter; the flesh, when fully ripe, is sweet and full of flavour. Unripe fruits taste rather sour.
COUNTRY OF ORIGIN: Peru, Brazil.
PRODUCER COUNTRIES: New Zealand, Southeast Asia, Brazil, Kenya.
AVAILABILITY: Almost all year round from various producer countries.

USE: Peel the fruit, eat the flesh (including the pips) fresh, with a little sugar to taste; use in desserts and fruit salads, cook together with meat, make into jam or chutney.
KEEPING QUALITIES: One or two days at room temperature.
NUTRITIONAL VALUE: 50 Kcal, 150 i.u. vitamin A and 25mg vitamin C per 100g serving.
INDUSTRIAL PROCESSING: None.

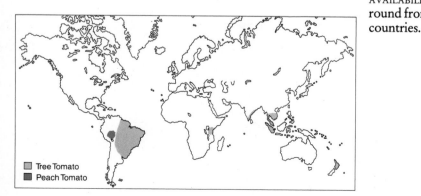

□ Tree Tomato
■ Peach Tomato

△ Cape Gooseberry, ⅔in (17mm) in diameter

Cape Gooseberry or Goldenberry
(Physalis peruviana)

DESCRIPTION: The actual berry is enclosed in a papery, orange-yellow 'Chinese lantern' 1½-2in (45-50mm) long; the berry itself is smaller. When fully ripe the berries are light green or orange-red. They have a smooth skin and contain small, soft, edible pips. Ripe berries taste pleasantly tart and smell a bit like pineapple.

COUNTRY OF ORIGIN: Peru.

PRODUCER COUNTRY: South Africa, Kenya, Madagascar, Southeast Asia.

AVAILABILITY: December to June.

USE: Eat berries fresh, including pips, or cut in half and use in fruit salads, jam, etc. To sweeten fresh fruits, prick a few holes in the skin, sprinkle with sugar and leave to absorb.

KEEPING QUALITIES: A few days at room temperature.

NUTRITIONAL VALUE: 40 Kcal, 3,000 i.u. vitamin A, 30mg vitamin C and 2.8mg vitamin B12 per 100g serving.

INDUSTRIAL PROCESSING: None.

Quito Orange
(Solanum quitoense)

DESCRIPTION: A round or slightly elongated fruit, 1¼-2½in (3-6cm) long and yellow to bright orange in colour. The skin is thick and leathery, and covered with short, stiff hairs that sometimes rub off during harvesting. The yellow-green flesh is divided into compartments filled with jelly-like flesh and numerous seeds. The taste is pleasingly sharp and aromatic.

COUNTRY OF ORIGIN: Colombia, Peru.

PRODUCER COUNTRIES: Colombia, Peru, Ecuador, Panama, Costa Rica, Guatemala, Thailand.

AVAILABILITY: Throughout the year (very irregular).

USE: Make into juice, jam or compote; always sieve or strain flesh to remove seeds and skin hairs.

KEEPING QUALITIES: A few days at room temperature.

NUTRITIONAL VALUE: 600 i.u. vitamin A and 25mg vitamin C per 100g serving.

INDUSTRIAL PROCESSING: Juice and concentrate.

△ Cannibal's Tomato (immature), 1¼in (30mm) long

Peach Tomato or *Cocoña*
(Solanum topiro)
DESCRIPTION: Spherical or oval fruit, up to 4in (10cm) in diameter. The skin is yellow or tomato red; the pale yellow flesh is deliciously sweet and thirst-quenching.
COUNTRIES OF ORIGIN: Amazonian region.
PRODUCER COUNTRY: Peru.
AVAILABILITY: Almost all year round, but very irregular.
USE: Make into juice or jam or use fresh in desserts.
KEEPING QUALITIES: A few days at room temperature.
NUTRITIONAL VALUE: Not known.
INDUSTRIAL PROCESSING: Juice and concentrate.

Melon Pear or **Tree Melon**
(Solanum muricatum)
DESCRIPTION: A pear-shaped, tapering fruit, up to 8in (20cm) long, with a thin skin that changes colour from off-white when unripe to pale yellow streaked with purple when ripe. The flesh is yellowish-white, juicy and sweet, and very seldom contains seeds. The taste is faintly reminiscent of pear, peach or melon.
COUNTRY OF ORIGIN: Peru, Colombia.
PRODUCER COUNTRIES: New Zealand, South Africa, Chile, Peru, Bolivia, Venezuela, Spain.
AVAILABILITY: Throughout the year.
USE: Eat fresh with or without skin; use in appetizers and desserts in much the same way as melon.
KEEPING QUALITIES: One week at room temperature.
NUTRITIONAL VALUE: Not known.
INDUSTRIAL PROCESSING: Canned.

Cannibal's Tomato
(Solanum uporo or
S. aculeatissimum)
DESCRIPTION: A small, round fruit, ¾-1¼in (2-3cm) in diameter, full of seeds, and red when fully ripe. Taste is similar to that of an ordinary tomato, only sweeter.
COUNTRIES OF ORIGIN: Northern part of South America.
PRODUCER COUNTRIES: As above; also Caribbean.
AVAILABILITY: April to June, but very irregular.
USE: Eat fresh or use as ordinary tomato.
KEEPING QUALITIES: A few days at room temperature.
NUTRITIONAL VALUE: Not known.
INDUSTRIAL PROCESSING: None.

Vitaceae
Grape

The *Vitaceae* or vine family has representatives in most parts of the world and includes nearly 450 species, but there is one species above all others that has fascinated people for millennia: *Vitis vinifera,* the grapevine.

After thousands of years of improvement, this woody climbing plant now provides a rich assortment of delicious fruits for eating and for wine-making. Grapes have been made into wine since 4000 BC, the date of the founding of the Mesopotamian city of Ur. From that time to this, wine has been of enormous social and commercial significance; indeed if you listen to the way it is discussed in some quarters you might conclude that it has some mysterious religious significance as well.

The significance of wine can be better appreciated by looking at what happens to the grape harvest each year. Five per cent of all the grapes grown each year are turned into juice; a further five per cent are turned into currants and raisins; another ten per cent are eaten as dessert grapes; and a monster eighty per cent are made into wines or into spirits such as brandy, cognac, armagnac, and so on.

The grapevine is thought to have come originally from the region around the Black Sea; certainly it seems to have been domesticated in that region from a wild form. It arrived in Western Europe quite late in its history, around 1500 BC, when Greek colonists began cultivating it in the Marseilles area of southern France. From there the grapevine followed the tramp of the Roman legions over most of Europe, landing nearly sixteen centuries later in the New World, via Haiti and Mexico. In the 19th century, American vines came to the rescue of the European wine industry: faced with annihilation of their vines by the dreaded *Phylloxera* beetle, European vine-growers grafted cuttings from unaffected vines onto American rootstocks, endowing the traditional European varieties with resistance to *Phylloxera*.

In this chapter we deal mainly with table grapes rather than wine grapes, and with varieties that come mainly from France, Italy, Germany, Spain, Greece, Israel, South Africa, United States and South America.

There is only one obvious difference between grapes grown under glass and grapes grown in the open, and that is that the skins of greenhouse grapes generally have an undamaged waxy outer layer. Grapes grown in the open tend to lose this layer in wind and rain long before they are harvested. This does not affect the quality of the fruit, only the appearance.

Grapes are generally described as being black or white. In fact, white grapes can be any shade between green and a transparent amber-yellow, and black grapes anything from red to deep blue-black. The taste of table grapes has a lot to do with their skins, which can be tough or tender, or high or low in tannin content. Some varieties have a pronounced musky scent, for instance muscatel grapes and some South African hybrids. Both scent and flavour depend to a great extent on the area where the grapes are grown, vines being very sensitive to climate and soil. Wines that can only be produced from grapes grown in a special area tend, if they are of any quality, to be very expensive. The more slowly grapes ripen, the richer their aroma. Grapes grown furthest from the Equator in both hemispheres are the most fragrant.

A well established vineyard in Egypt

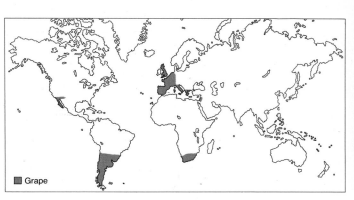

■ Grape

△ Alphonse Lavallée, 1 in (24mm) diameter

Grape
(Vitis vinifera)
DESCRIPTION: Spherical or oval fruits, $\frac{1}{2}$ -$1\frac{1}{4}$in (1-3cm) in diameter, that grow in bunches. Blue-black, green or red in colour, often with a pronounced surface bloom (yeasts living on the surface of the skin). The greenish-white flesh contains several pips. The taste varies from sour to very sweet, depending on the variety. The skin is edible, though it can be somewhat tough and bitter, and so are the pips, although most people spit them out.

COUNTRIES OF ORIGIN: Caucasus region.
PRODUCER COUNTRIES: France, Italy, Spain, Greece, South Africa, Israel, United States, South America.
AVAILABILITY: Throughout the year from various producer countries.
USE: Eat raw, use in fruit salads, squeeze for juice.
KEEPING QUALITIES: Generally about four days at room temperature; a little longer in the refrigerator.
NUTRITIONAL VALUE: 75 Kcal, 5mg vitamin C, and traces of vitamins A and B per 100g serving.

INDUSTRIAL PROCESSING: Juice, concentrate, wine, fortified wines, spirits, currants and raisins.

Black Varieties

Alphonse Lavallée and **Red River** Although there is no significant difference between these two varieties, the trade still differentiates between them. 'Alphonse Lavallée', which comes mainly from southern Europe, Israel and South Africa, is blue-black in colour, while 'Red River' (or just 'River') from United States and South America tends to be

on the reddish side. Colour variations are probably due to differences in climate and soil; if grown in South Africa, for example, 'Red River' produces blue-black grapes. Both varieties have large, very juicy grapes and a tender skin that splits cleanly as you bite into it.

△ Red River, 1in (26mm) diameter

Barlinka Exported from South Africa between February and June. A deep blue-black variety with large, more or less spherical fruits. Juicy, sweet-tasting and strongly scented. Grows in plump, attractive bunches.

Black Beauty The earliest of all the black varieties grown in United States. Very popular because it is seedless. Fruits are medium to large, lusciously juicy. Available in May and early June.

Cardinal A cross between 'Tokay' and 'Red River', and grown in many countries, including United States and South America, France, Italy, Spain and South Africa. Generally available between June and December. The grapes are more red than black, and more or less spherical. Juicy, very sweet, with a musky note. 'Cardinal Rosata' is an Italian variety, lighter in colour than 'Cardinal', and with a thinner skin.

△ Barlinka, 1in (29mm) diameter   ▽ Cardinal, ¾in (20mm) diameter

△ Frankenthaler, 1in (23mm) diameter.

△ Red Emperor, ⅔in (21mm) diameter

Frankenthaler The ancestry of this variety is not known, but it is thought to have originated in Germany or Italy. Mainly exported from Belgium and Netherlands, where it is grown under glass. Appears on the market between mid-September and early December. The first bunches are ready for picking as early as May. Moderately-sized grapes, with a thin skin, blue-black with a faint bloom, and very sweet. 'Frankenthalers' that are less than fully ripe are red or greenish-red rather than blue-black.

Gros Maroc Although the name implies that this is a variety which comes from North Africa, it is in fact a European hothouse variety and was developed in England. The blue-black grapes grow in short, broad bunches, and have an attractive bloom. The taste is excellent, though the consistency is very soft.

Available from October to December, but specimens picked early in the season are often under-ripe and the flavour suffers accordingly.

Olivette Noire Also called 'Pizzutello Nera' in Italy. A longish, blue-black grape rather like an olive. The berries are sweet and rather squashy. Exported in August and November, mainly from France. Italian production is mainly for domestic consumption.

Red Emperor A late-season variety widely grown in California, Argentina, Chile and South Africa. Medium-sized, red fruits with a distinctive cherry flavour. Bunches tend to be somewhat straggly, but travel well. Available September to April.

Royal A black grape, probably a close relative of 'Alphonse Lavallée', developed and grown under glass in Belgium. Grows in long, fat, heavy bunches. The grapes are large, reddish-purple, firm-skinned, and have a black wax layer. They are also full of juice, sweet, and exceptionally fragrant. Available between October and April.

West Frisia A Dutch greenhouse grape, developed around 1930. Grows in very large bunches and has robust, longish, purple-black fruits. The skin is soft and bursts crisply as you bite into it. Sweet, juicy and full of flavour. Available between July and October.

△ Royal, 1in (27mm) diameter ▽ West Frisia, 1in (27mm) diameter

White Varieties

Almeria Also known as 'Ohanes' or 'Ohanez'. A variety which also has a black counterpart. White 'Almerias' are fairly large, firm-fleshed and firm-skinned, but taste somewhat bland. Exported from Spain and Italy. Available from October to April.

Golden Champion A white greenhouse grape developed in England in 1853 and now mainly grown in England and Netherlands. Attractive amber-green, translucent fruits which grow in longish, conical bunches. The skin is so thin that when the grapes are ripe the pips can be seen through it. Sweet and easy to eat. Available between October and January.

△ Almeria, 1 in (27mm) diameter

△ Golden Champion, 1¼in (30mm) diameter

△ Italia, 1¼in (30mm) diameter

△ Muscatel, ¾in (20mm) diameter

△ Regina, 1in (25mm) diameter ▽ Queen of the Vineyard, 1in (24mm) diameter

Italia Related to 'Muscatel' and also known as 'Roman Muscatel'. Mainly exported from Italy, France and Greece between August and November. Grows in very long bunches sometimes weighing over 4lb (2kg). The grapes are very large, yellow or yellowish-green, and sweet with a distinct smell of musk; they burst crisply when you bite into them.

Muscatel A Mediterranean variety (France, Italy, Spain), but also grown under glass further north. The yellowish-green berries are generally oval and have a sweet, musky flavour. The yellower the colour, the stronger the musky note. Available between September and January.

Queen of the Vineyard Also called 'Regina dei Vigneti' in Italy. The biggest exporters of this variety are Italy, Israel and South Africa. Available between September and November, in July, and also January and February. The rather large and slightly oval fruits are yellow or greenish-yellow, sweet-tasting and have a pronounced musky fragrance.

△Rosaki, ⅔in (18mm) diameter

△Sultana, ½in (12mm) diameter

Rosaki Considerable confusion surrounds this very sweet grape. In the first place, it is traded under many names: the Greeks call it 'Rosaki', the Italians call it 'Regina Bianca', 'Regina della Puglia' or 'Puglia', and in Syria it is called 'Dattier de Beyrouth'. And to make things even more confusing, the taste and colour of 'Rosaki' grapes vary according to the soil and climate in producing areas. Colour, for example, varies from green through greenish-yellow to yellowish-brown. 'Rosaki' grapes are oval, thin-skinned and generally very sweet, sometimes with a hint of muskiness. Main producer countries are Greece, Italy, Spain, France, Israel, South Africa and South America. Available August to April.

Sultana One of the seedless grape varieties used for drying (sultanas) but also very popular as a dessert grape. The fruits are small, firm, juicy and sweet-tasting. Exported between June and March from many different producer countries. Other seedless varieties related to 'Sultana' are 'Thompson Seedless', 'Sultanina' and 'Perlette'.

Thompson Seedless Easily the most important variety of table grape grown in United States. Fruits are pale green and pleasantly sweet without being cloying. Available June to August.

Waltham Cross and **New Cross** Two very closely related, white varieties imported exclusively from South Africa in February and March. The grapes are greenish-yellow, thin-skinned and sweet. Little is known about the origin of these two rather idiosyncratic species. Some experts regard them as descendants of the American variety 'Niagara', others as an improved version of 'Regina'.

RECIPES

The main aim of the recipe section which follows is to suggest novel ways of preparing less well-known fruits. Apart from basic instructions for making jams, jellies, chutneys and fruit salads, most cookbooks ignore the possibilities of cooking with exotic fruits. Recipes that put them to imaginative use only tend to develop when master chefs turn their attention to them. Even so, fruit often plays only a minor part in elaborate dishes.

All the recipes which follow use fresh fruit, all of them have been tested, and **all quantities are for four people.** Whether your taste is for the sweet or savoury, the light or substantial, the simple or elaborate, *bon appétit.*

Avocado and guava dessert

4 fresh guavas	sugar
1 large avocado	cream
1 orange	½ cup/4fl oz/125g quark or set
1 tablespoon sugar	yoghurt or full fat soft cheese
juice of ½ lemon	vanilla flavouring

Peel and dice avocado and guavas. Mix with orange segments, adding sugar and lemon juice to taste. Chill. Sweeten cream with sugar, add vanilla flavouring, and blend with quark/yoghurt/soft cheese. Place alternate layers of cream and fruit in a bowl or glass dish and decorate with orange slices.

Cream of avocado soup

2 large ripe avocados	1 egg yolk
4½ cups/1¾pints/1l	4 tablespoons cream
chicken stock	salt
¼ cup/1½oz/40g butter	freshly-ground pepper
1 tablespoon/1oz/30g flour	

Peel, halve and stone avocados, and mash flesh through a fine sieve. Bring stock to boil, and stir in paste made of flour and melted butter to thicken it. Stir in sieved avocado and season with salt and pepper.

Blend egg yolk and cream with a little of the stock, then stir into the rest. Remove pan from heat and serve. A third avocado could be cut into thin strips and used to garnish.

Chicken ragoût with avocado

1lb/500g lean cooked	¼ teaspoon curry powder
chicken meat	1 glass medium dry sherry
2 large avocados	salt and freshly-ground pepper
2oz/50g butter	1 egg yolk
2oz/50g flour	3 tablespoons cream
1 tablespoon chopped onion/	2½ cups/1 pint/500ml chicken
shallot	stock

Dice chicken meat. Halve, peel and stone avocados, and dice to same size as chicken. Melt butter in a frying pan, and fry chopped onion/shallot. Add flour and curry powder and mix to a smooth paste. Add sherry and sufficient chicken stock to produce a thick sauce, stirring continuously over a low heat. Season sauce to taste. Add diced chicken. Blend egg yolk and cream together until smooth, thin with a little sauce, then stir into rest of sauce. Remove pan from heat and stir in chopped avocado. Serve in vol-au-vent cases, or on a bed of rice, or with bread.

Avocado eggs

4 hard-boiled eggs
1 ripe avocado
1 tablespoon yoghurt
½ teaspoon grated lemon
*   peel*
4 tomatoes
1 head blanched celery
lettuce
parsley
salt and pepper

Halve eggs lengthways, remove yolk and chop finely. Halve and pit avocado, peel, then purée avocado flesh. Add egg yolk, yoghurt and lemon peel to purée and season with salt and pepper.

Fill halved eggs with avocado mixture, topping each with a slice of tomato. Serve on a bed of celery matchsticks and the rest of the tomatoes. Garnish with parsley as a final touch.

Chicken, date and avocado salad

3 large ripe avocados
2 tart apples
1¼ cups/9oz/250g chicken meat
16 fresh dates
2 tablespoons mayonnaise
pinch of curry powder
1 tablespoon lemon juice/
*   spiced vinegar*
shelled walnuts or hazelnuts

Peel avocados, remove stones, and dice flesh. Peel and core apples, dice and mix with chopped avocado. Sprinkle with lemon juice to prevent discoloration.

Dice chicken. Halve and pit dates. Add chicken and dates to apples and avocados. Add curry powder, salt and pepper to mayonnaise and stir into the salad mixture. Serve on a bed of crisp, chopped lettuce with a scattering of coarsely-chopped nuts over the top.

Lentils with apricots

2oz/50g fresh apricots
8oz/250g lentils
2 onions
4 walnuts
1 tablespoon chopped parsley
2oz/50g butter
pepper and salt

Wash lentils and soak overnight in plenty of water. Skin and pit apricots. Finely chop onions. Brown onions in butter and add chopped apricots. Bring lentils to the boil, then add all the other ingredients, including seasonings and chopped walnuts, and simmer until lentils are just soft and have absorbed most of the cooking liquid. Serve garnished with the chopped parsley.

Apples with rum

4 large/8 small apples
4 tablespoons runny honey
2 tablespoons rum
¼ cup/2oz/50g raisins
1 teaspoon cornflour
redcurrant jelly or red jam
½ cup/4fl oz/100ml water

Peel, halve and core apples. Put in a pan with the water and simmer gently until the apples begin to soften. Add honey and cream, letting the liquid soak into the apples, which must not break up.

As soon as apples are glazed (5-7 minutes), drain and place on a dish. Soak raisins in cooking liquid, then arrange on the halved apples.

Thicken remaining liquid with the cornflour. Pour thickened sauce over apples and raisins, and garnish with jelly or jam. Serve as a dessert or as an accompaniment to semolina or creamed rice.

Roast beef and banana fingers

8 slices cold roast beef
4 bananas
1 teaspoon lemon juice
mustard

Make sure roast beef is rare and thinly sliced. Peel bananas and sprinkle with lemon juice. Halve them lengthways and roll each half in a slice of beef. Secure with a cocktail stick.

Banana pancakes

1 cup/8fl oz/250ml milk
4 eggs
pinch salt
2 cups/7oz/200g flour
6-8 bananas
butter
castor sugar
lemon juice

Make batter with eggs, salt, flour, milk and water. Heat butter in frying pan. Pour a spoonful of batter into the pan and allow to spread. Add small slices of banana. Turn the pancake and brown on the other side. Serve sprinkled with castor sugar and lemon juice.

Chicory, ham and banana bake

5 small cooking bananas
8 small heads chicory
8 slices cooked ham
1 cup/½ pint/250ml cheese sauce

Clean chicory, boil or steam until just tender, and drain.
Place one chicory head and half a peeled banana (sliced
lengthways) on each slice of ham. Roll up ham and place in
a buttered ovenproof dish. Pour cheese sauce over ham
rolls, cover and cook in a moderate oven for 30 minutes
(uncover for last 10 minutes to allow sauce to brown).

Rice ring with crab and bananas

1 cup/8oz/250g rice   *salt*
2 tablespoons/1oz/30g butter   *lemon juice*
nutmeg   *knob butter*
½ cup/¼ pint/100ml meat stock   *1 cup/7oz/200g crabmeat*
½ cup/¼ pint/100ml milk   *4 bananas*
½ teaspoon cornflour   *2 tomatoes*

Cook rice in salted water, strain, rinse and leave to drain.
Melt butter and mix into rice; season with salt and
nutmeg. Shape rice into a ring, preferably in a mould, chill
and turn out onto a large flat dish.
    Heat stock and milk gently, and blend in cornflour.
Season with salt and lemon juice and stir in knob of butter,
then the crumbled crabmeat. Add bananas, sliced into thin
rounds. Chill.
    Heap up crab and banana mixture inside rice ring.
Garnish with banana rounds and tomato slices.

Blueberry or bilberry pie

2 cups/1lb/500g fresh   *5oz/150g sweet pie dough*
* blueberries or bilberries* *1 egg*
2-4 tablespoons sugar

Wash berries, removing stalks, and put in a greased pie
dish. Sprinkle with 2-4 tablespoons sugar to taste.
    Roll out dough on a floured surface. Cut out pie 'lid' to
fit pie dish, and also a strip of dough to cover the rim of the
dish. Moisten strip around rim and cover with lid, pressing
them together. Make cuts or fork marks to give a
decorative edge. Brush with beaten egg to glaze. Bake for
30-40 minutes in a moderate oven until pie crust is crisp
and golden-brown.

Baked bananas with coconut

4 slightly under-ripe bananas   *butter*
1 spoonful sugar
juice of one lemon   *1½ tablespoons Kirsch liqueur*
2 tablespoons freshly-grated   *1½ tablespoons Pisang Ambon*
* coconut*   * liqueur (or dry sherry)*

Peel bananas, halve them lengthways and lay flat side
down on a flat dish. Sprinkle with sugar, lemon juice and
coconut, and leave for 1 hour. Melt a small knob of butter
in a frying pan and cook bananas on both sides (rounded
side first) for about 7 minutes. Mix Kirsch and Pisang
Ambon, heat in a ladle over a low heat and pour over the
bananas. Flambé either in the kitchen or at the table,
serving bananas straight from the cooking dish.

Roast meat with coconut milk

1¼ cup/10fl oz/250ml
  coconut milk
1 clove garlic
1 medium onion
2 tablespoons olive oil

1lb/500g beef (large chunks)
cayenne pepper
ground ginger
ground coriander
salt and pepper

Finely chop onion. Fry in olive oil in a large pan until light brown, adding whole clove of garlic. Remove garlic and add beef chunks to onion. Brown chunks all over and add cayenne, ginger and coriander. Leave to simmer a little longer before adding coconut milk. Set pan on low heat and cook until meat is tender (this will depend on quality of meat, but allow about 1 hour). Serve with bread or rice.

Baked cherimoyas

3 cherimoyas
lemon juice or rum
2 egg yolks
½ cup/5fl oz/125ml white wine
pinch salt
¼ cup/2½oz/60g sugar

1 cup/5oz/150g flour
2 tablespoons melted butter
2 egg whites
oil or butter
icing sugar

Peel cherimoyas and cut into slices. Remove black seeds. Sprinkle fruit with lemon juice and leave to absorb. Make a thick pouring batter with egg yolks, wine, sugar, salt and flour. Fold in the stiffly-beaten egg whites. Dip cherimoya slices in batter, then fry in butter or oil until golden-brown on both sides. Sprinkle with icing sugar and serve.

Cherimoya cream

2 glasses milk
1-2 cherimoyas
2 egg yolks
2 tablespoons sugar

1½ tablespoons flour
lemon juice
salt
melted chocolate for topping

Peel cherimoyas, remove seeds, and slice. Mix egg yolks, sugar and flour together in a bowl; add lemon juice and a pinch of salt. Add cherimoya slices to the mixture and stir in milk. Bring gently to the boil, then allow to cool.

Divide cherimoya cream between four glasses and top with a little melted chocolate.

Cherimoya mousse

1 large cherimoya
juice of one orange
white wine

4 ice cubes
4 slices orange

Halve the cherimoya, spoon out flesh and remove seeds. Purée flesh in a mixer or blender with orange juice. Take four glasses, put an ice cube in each and divide the mousse between them. Add two tablespoons white wine to each glass and top with slice of orange.

Cranberry cake

1 cup/8oz/225g puréed
  cranberries
6oz/175g castor sugar
1lb/450g flour
grated orange peel
4 tablespoons baking powder

3oz/75g chopped nuts
1 cup/½ pt/225ml milk
1 beaten egg
2 tablespoons melted butter
salt

Mix cranberries with a quarter of the sugar. Stir in remaining sugar, flour, baking powder and a little salt. Add nuts and orange peel. Mix together milk, egg and butter and stir thoroughly into dry ingredients. Pour into a greased 8in (20cm) cake tin and bake in a moderate oven.

Honeyed cranberries

4 cups/2lb/1kg fresh
  cranberries
1lb/500g apples
1½ cups/12fl oz/300ml honey
1 cup/8oz/250g sugar
peel of ½ orange

peel of ½ lemon
1 teaspoon cinnamon
1 teaspoon dry/freshly-
  grated ginger
2 tablespoons rum

Wash cranberries and drain. Wash and grate apples. Mix cranberries and apple with honey and sugar. Bring to the boil, stirring continuously, and cook until the mixture reaches setting point (test by dropping teaspoonful on chilled plate). Add finely-chopped orange and lemon peel, cinnamon, dry or freshly-grated ginger and rum. Cook for a few more minutes, then pour into sterilized screw-topped jars. Use as a spread or as a relish with roast meats, poultry and game.

Date compote

1 cup/½lb/250g fresh dates
white wine
2-3 cloves

whipped cream
sugar

Stone dates; put in a pan with cloves, and add white wine to cover. Cook on a low heat for about 20 minutes. Add sugar to taste. Serve cold with whipped cream.

Date loaf

1 cup/½lb/250g fresh dates
½ cup/5oz/150g flour
¼ cup/3oz/100g sugar
2 tablespoons Grand Marnier
  liqueur
3 eggs

vanilla flavouring
1¼ cups/10oz/300g shelled
  mixed nuts
⅛ cup/2oz/50g mixed dried fruit
⅛ cup/2oz/50g raisins
butter
milk

Soak raisins in Grand Marnier for half an hour. Coarsely chop nuts. Beat eggs with sugar and vanilla until fluffy and fold flour in lightly. Add finely-chopped dates, nuts, dried fruit and liqueur-soaked raisins. Mix to a soft consistency, adding a little milk if necessary, and pour into a well-buttered loaf pan. Bake in a preheated oven (350°F/175°C) for about 1½ hours. Serve in thin slices.

Chicken with dates

1 chicken
1 cup/9oz/250g minced veal and chicken liver
½lb/250g fresh dates
1 tablespoon honey
½ cup/4oz/150g flour
salt and freshly-ground pepper
1 can mandarin oranges in syrup
¾ cup/7fl oz/200ml dry white wine
6 tablespoons/4fl oz/100ml fresh cream

Fry minced veal and chicken liver in butter, and season with salt and pepper. Stone dates, chop half finely and add to mince mixture. Season inside of chicken with salt and pepper, stuff with mince mixture and sew opening. Baste skin with honey.

Melt butter in frying pan and brown chicken all over. Transfer chicken to preheated oven and cook for about 45 minutes at 400°F/200°C, basting frequently. Take chicken out of oven and keep warm.

Pour off fat from cooking juices and mix remainder with white wine and a few tablespoons of mandarin syrup. Simmer gently for about 10 minutes, then add mandarin segments and rest of dates. Add fresh cream, allow to thicken, then spoon over chicken. Serve with boiled rice.

Tea and fig cream

4 eggs
3 tablespoons/4oz/100g sugar
6 tablespoons strong hot tea
1 tablespoon lemon juice
6 figs
1 teaspoon gelatine
ground pistachio nuts

Beat egg yolks with sugar until frothy. Soak gelatine in cold water, dissolve in hot tea. Mix tea and gelatine with lemon juice, chopped figs and beaten egg mixture. As mixture begins to thicken, fold in stiffly-whipped egg whites. Sprinkle with ground pistachio nuts and serve chilled.

Fig soufflé

10 green figs
11oz/300g raspberries
3 egg whites
2 egg yolks
1½ cups/7oz/200g icing sugar
3 tablespoons sweetened cream
2 tablespoons raspberry liqueur
1 teaspoon lemon juice
1 cup/7oz/200g cornflour
butter

Beat egg yolks with three-quarters of the sugar until frothy. Wash and sieve figs. Mix fig pulp with cornflour and beaten egg mixture. Add sweetened cream, one tablespoon raspberry liqueur and lemon juice. Mix well. Beat egg whites until very stiff, then fold into fruit mixture.

Pour soufflé mixture into a greased ovenproof dish and bake in a preheated oven for 30 minutes until soufflé has risen.

Meanwhile sieve the raspberries, mix with remaining sugar and raspberry liqueur and put mixture in freezer compartment of refrigerator. Serve the soufflé hot with a topping of chilled raspberry purée.

Baked figs

12 figs
2 tablespoons water
½ cup/5fl oz/125ml thick cream
2 teaspoons rum
2 tablespoons/2oz/50g brown sugar

Rub bloom off figs and prick with a fork. Cover base of an ovenproof dish with water, add figs, sprinkle sugar on top and bake for 30 minutes in a preheated oven (400°F/200°C). Spoon sugar syrup over figs from time to time. Leave to cool. Whip cream until stiff and mix in rum. Decorate figs with whipped cream.

Fresh fig dessert

16 fresh black figs
1 cup/8fl oz/250ml thick cream
4 tablespoons fresh raspberries
raspberry liqueur (optional)

Peel figs and cut into quarters. Divide fruit among four dessert bowls and sprinkle with liqueur. Sieve raspberries, mix with cream and pour over figs. Serve chilled.

Breast of lamb with grapefruit stuffing

2 breasts of lamb (1lb/500g of meat)
1¼ cups/8oz/225g fresh breadcrumbs
1 large onion
6 tablespoons/3oz/75g butter
3 grapefruits
2 tablespoons chopped mint
2 tablespoons chopped parsley
1 egg
pepper and salt

Sauté finely-chopped onion in two-thirds of the butter until transparent. Add breadcrumbs, chopped flesh of two of the grapefruits, chopped mint and parsley, beaten egg, salt and pepper. Mix well. Spread just over half of this mixture onto the first breast of lamb and roll it up into a sausage shape; spread the rest over the second breast of lamb and wrap it, stuffing on the inside, around the first. Secure with string.

Put the rolled lamb into a roasting pan, season the outside and dot with remaining butter. Preheat oven to 350°F/180°C and roast for 1 hour. Raise heat to 400°F/200°C and roast for a further 20 minutes, basting from time to time. Garnish with skinned segments of the third grapefruit before slicing and serving.

Grapefruit with fennel

2 grapefruits
2 small bulbs fennel
½ cup/5fl oz/125ml sour cream
3oz/75g grated Emmental cheese
pepper and salt

Cut grapefruits in half, scoop out flesh and cut into chunks. Grate fennel. Stir fruit and fennel into sour cream, add grated cheese and a little salt and pepper. Put this filling into the empty grapefruit halves and chill well before serving.

Veal steaks with guava

4 veal steaks (4oz/120g each)
8 fresh guavas
2 eggs
1 cup/4oz/100g grated coconut
ginger, dry or freshly grated
ground coriander
salt and pepper
oil or butter
lemon juice to taste

Peel and dice guavas. Season steaks well on both sides with salt, pepper and coriander. Dip steaks in beaten egg, sprinkle with coconut, and cook on both sides in hot butter or oil. Keep steaks warm.

Coat diced guava with beaten egg, sprinkle with coconut and bake in a moderate oven until light brown. Add ginger to taste, and perhaps a squeeze of lemon. Spread baked fruit on steaks and serve with boiled rice.

Guava nectar

3 fresh guavas
orange peel
sugar

Wash and dice guavas; cover guava and strips of orange peel with boiling water. Leave to stand for a few minutes. Sieve and sweeten with sugar to taste. Serve chilled.

Grapefruit sorbet

2-3 red grapefruits
¾ cup/6oz/175g sugar
1 cup/8fl oz/250ml dry
    white wine
juice of one lemon
2 tablespoons
    Campari
2 egg whites
2 tablespoons water

Boil sugar and water to make a syrup and allow to cool. Squeeze grapefruits and mix juice with lemon juice. Sieve juice and add wine, Campari and sugar syrup. Beat egg whites until stiff and fold thoroughly into juice mixture. Freeze, beating mixture from time to time to make sure it stays frothy.

Citrus fruit soufflé

1 grapefruit
2 oranges
1 cup/8oz/225g sugar
1 cup/8fl oz/250ml thick cream
½oz/15g gelatine
4 tablespoons water
2 tablespoons chopped almonds
3 eggs

Separate eggs, putting yolks into a pan with sugar and grated peel of the grapefruit and of one of the oranges. Add juice of half the grapefruit and of the peeled orange. Stand pan in a larger pan filled with enough hot water to come half-way up the smaller pan and cook mixture over a low heat until thick and foamy. Remove from heat and beat from time to time as mixture cools.

Add stiffly whipped cream and gelatine (dissolved in cold water beforehand). Pour into a soufflé dish and leave in a cool place to set. Decorate with chopped almonds and slices or segments of the second orange.

Kumquat cocktail

ice cubes
1½ measures Campari
1 measure vodka
1 bottle bitter orange
5 kumquats

Put 7 or 8 ice cubes in a tall jug, add vodka, Campari and bitter orange. Prick kumquats in several places, put in jug and allow to stand for 30 minutes while the cocktail absorbs the flavour of the kumquats. Chill thoroughly, remove the kumquats, and pour into four tall glasses.

Kumquats in wine jelly

4oz/100g kumquats
2 tablespoons sugar
juice of one lemon
5 rounded teaspoons gelatine
water
3 tablespoons sugar
1¼ cups/10fl oz/250ml red wine
½ cup/5fl oz/125ml whipped
    cream
2 tablespoons grated coconut

Slice kumquats and simmer gently with 2 tablespoons sugar in about ⅔ cup/5fl oz/150ml water for 10 minutes. Drain and reserve juice. Dissolve gelatine in ⅔ pint/ 12fl oz/350ml hot water, and add the kumquat juice, lemon juice, the rest of the sugar, and the red wine. Divide kumquat slices between four glasses and pour over jelly liquid. When set, decorate with whipped cream and grated coconut.

Poultry salad with kiwi fruit

10oz/300g cooked chicken or
  turkey meat
2 kiwi fruits
1 can mandarin orange
  segments
4 tablespoons mayonnaise
Angostura bitters
2 tablespoons yoghurt
salt and pepper
lettuce

Dice poultry meat and season to taste. Peel kiwi fruits, then slice or dice them. Mix meat and fruit with mandarin segments. Blend together mayonnaise, yoghurt, a tablespoon of mandarin juice, a little salt and a dash of Angostura, and pour over meat/fruit mixture. Arrange on lettuce leaves.

Kiwi bavarois with Advocaat sauce

5 kiwi fruits
1 cup/9fl oz/250ml white wine
3 tablespoons/2oz/40g
  cornflour
1 cup/9fl oz/250ml apple juice
3 tablespoons/3oz/75g sugar
thin sliver of orange peel
pulp of one vanilla pod
1½ tablespoons Curaçao liqueur
⅔ cup/5fl oz/150ml
  sour cream
4 tablespoons Advocaat liqueur
sugar
vanilla flavouring

Peel kiwi fruits and dice, reserving four slices for decoration. Mix cornflour with a third of the wine. Bring remaining wine, apple juice, sugar, orange, peel and pulp from vanilla pod to the boil; stir in wine and cornflour mix and allow to thicken. Remove pan from heat, take out orange peel and add Curaçao. Allow to cool a little. Purée two thirds of diced kiwi fruit, then add this, with the rest of the diced fruit to the thickened juice and mix thoroughly. Divide mixture between four glasses and chill in refrigerator.

Blend sour cream and Advocaat thoroughly. Sweeten to taste with sugar and a little vanilla flavouring and pour over chilled bavarois just before serving. Decorate with the reserved kiwi slices.

Fillet steak with kiwi

4 fillet steaks
4 kiwi fruits
2 tablespoons butter
pepper and salt

A few minutes before cooking, rub steaks with the cut surface of a halved kiwi fruit, pressing gently so that the juice runs over the meat. Melt butter in a pan and brown steaks on both sides (about 3 minutes per side). Season with salt and pepper. Peel and slice the other kiwi fruits and cook with the steaks for a few minutes, turning once.

Raw fish in lime marinade

4 fillets sole or other white fish
6 large cooked prawns
6 limes
3 tomatoes
cayenne pepper
salt

Skin fillets and place on flat dish. Sprinkle with salt and a pinch of cayenne. Squeeze five of the limes and pour juice over fish. Marinate for 4 hours, turning occasionally.

Fifteen minutes before serving, drain fish well and arrange on a clean plate. Garnish with prawns, slices of tomato, and thin rounds cut from the remaining lime. Serve with vegetable crudités (matchstick carrots, scallions, cauliflower florets, cucumber slices, etc.).

Lychees with walnut cream stuffing

12 lychees
3 tablespoons quark (or full fat
  soft cheese)
3 tablespoons cream
1 tablespoon ground walnuts
white pepper
salt

Peel and pit lychees. Blend quark (or soft cheese), cream and walnuts to a smooth paste and season to taste. Fill hollowed out lychees with this and serve with unsalted crackers and dry sherry. (Most creamy cheeses, with or without a nut flavouring, go well with lychees.)

Chinese pancakes with lychees

24 lychees
3 tablespoons/3oz/80g flour
2 eggs
1 cup/8fl oz/225ml milk
1 tablespoon sugar
1 tablespoon Grand Marnier
  liqueur
2 tablespoons lemon juice
salt
icing sugar
butter

Put flour and salt in a bowl, add eggs and blend with milk to a smooth batter. Make pancakes. Peel and pit lychees and put into a pan with 2 tablespoons butter and 1 tablespoon sugar. Add liqueur and lemon juice and leave to simmer. Fold pancakes in half and then in half again, putting a little lychee mix in each. Arrange on a dish and pour the rest of the lychee syrup over them. Sprinkle with icing sugar and serve as hot as possible.

Mangosteen sorbet

6 mangosteens
1 egg white
2 tablespoons/2oz/50g sugar
$\frac{2}{3}$ cup/5fl oz/150ml champagne
  (or sparkling white wine)
6 slices of lime
strawberry sauce

Peel and dice mangosteens; sieve. Mix mangosteen pulp with champagne. Beat egg white until stiff, adding sugar gradually. Fold egg white into fruit pulp. Freeze, stirring occasionally so that the mixture remains light and frothy. Serve decorated with slices of lime and a dash of strawberry sauce.

Chicken breasts with mango

4 chicken breasts
2 mangoes
2 eggs
6 tablespoons/5oz/150g
  chopped almonds
4oz/120g butter
6 tablespoons thick cream
2 tablespoons flour
mango chutney
pepper and salt
curry powder to taste

Flatten chicken breasts and season with salt and pepper. Dip in flour, then into beaten egg, then into chopped almonds. Sauté in butter until golden brown all over.

Peel mangoes and cut flesh into thickish strips. Remove chicken from pan and keep warm. Heat mango strips, adding mango chutney, and salt and pepper to taste. Pour mango mixture over chicken. Season stiffly whipped cream with curry powder and use to garnish. Serve with boiled rice.

Mangoes with chocolate sauce

3 mangoes
4oz/100g bitter (dark)
  chocolate
$\frac{1}{4}$ cup/2fl oz/50ml cream
1 tablespoon water

Peel mangoes and cut into quarters. Break up chocolate, add water, and heat gently. Just before serving, stir in cream and pour over mango pieces.

Mango chutney

4 half-ripe mangoes
2 cooking apples
$\frac{1}{2}$ cup/4oz/100g raisins
1 onion
3 tablespoons/2oz/50g
  chopped crystallized ginger
1 clove garlic
1 teaspoon cayenne pepper
$\frac{1}{4}$ teaspoon ground cumin
1 tablespoon lemon juice
1 cup/8fl oz/225ml malt
  vinegar
$\frac{1}{2}$ cup/4oz/100g sugar
2 tablespoons ginger syrup
1 teaspoon salt

Discard fruit peel, pits and cores. Chop fruit and onion finely, and add finely-chopped ginger. Press garlic in garlic press and add. Bring all ingredients (except half the vinegar, the sugar and the ginger syrup) to the boil and simmer for about 1 hour. Add sugar, ginger syrup and rest of vinegar, and boil until chutney reaches setting point, stirring continuously. Pour into sterilized jars and seal well. Keep in a cool, dry place.

Stewed mangoes

3 mangoes
4 tablespoons/4oz/100g sugar
½ lemon

1 cup/8fl oz/225ml water
pinch cornflour
lemon juice

Peel mangoes, and cut flesh away from stones in longish chunks. Make a syrup with the sugar and water, adding lemon juice or finely grated lemon peel. Cook mango pieces for 5 minutes in hot syrup (which must not boil) until glazed. Remove fruit carefully from pan. Reduce syrup and thicken by stirring in cornflour mixed with a little water. Pour syrup over fruit and serve.

Melon with chicken

1 sweet melon
8oz/250g chicken breast
5oz/125g grapes or 3oz/75g
    raisins
5oz/125g chopped pineapple

2 tablespoons mayonnaise
4 tablespoons plain yoghurt
ground ginger
curry powder
salt and pepper

Simmer chicken in salted water until tender, adding a chicken stock cube if desired, and then chop the meat. Halve melon and remove pips. Remove some of the flesh and chop. Halve and remove pips from grapes. Blend yoghurt and mayonnaise, and add to chicken, melon, pineapple and grapes. Add ginger and curry powder to taste. Chill the mixture. Sprinkle inside of melon halves with ginger and curry powder. Fill melon 'baskets' with chilled chicken and fruit mixture.

Melon Alaska

2 small ripe melons
3 egg whites
4 scoops vanilla ice-cream
pinch salt

3 tablespoons/4oz/100g icing
    sugar
whole blanched almonds to
    decorate

Halve melons and remove pips. Cut a slice off the base of each half so that it does not roll around. Whip egg whites with salt until stiff, gradually adding sugar until the mixture stands up in peaks. Put a scoop of vanilla ice-cream into each melon half, and fill with beaten egg whites. Decorate with almonds. Cook in the hottest possible oven (500°F/250°C) until egg whites turn golden-brown. Serve straight from oven.

Stuffed melon

2 melons (1lb/500g each)
juice and grated peel of
    one orange

3 tablespoons/4oz/100g sugar
2 tablespoons Bénédictine
    liqueur

Halve melons and remove pips, saving as much of the juice as possible. Remove flesh with a spoon or melon-baller, taking care not to puncture the skin. Heat melon and orange juice with sugar and orange peel for about 3 minutes. Fill melon halves with fruit balls. Cool fruit syrup and mix with Bénédictine. Pour over the fruit. Serve well chilled.

Medlar jelly

1lb/500g medlars

preserving sugar

Wash medlars and cover with water, bring to boil and cook for 10 minutes. Mash them and allow to strain through muslin. To every 2½ cups/1 pint/600ml of strained juice add just under 1lb/450g preserving sugar. Boil until setting point is reached (about 45 minutes). Pour into preheated sterilized jars and seal well. A tasty accompaniment to roast lamb or pork.

Sole with orange

4 sole fillets
1 tablespoon orange juice
1 beaten egg

2½oz/60g butter
seasoned flour
parsley

Wash fish fillets and pat dry. Dip in seasoned flour and beaten egg. Melt half the butter in a frying pan and cook fish until butter begins to froth. Put cooked fish on a plate and keep warm. Melt remaining butter, add orange juice and pour sauce over fish immediately. Garnish with orange slices and chopped parsley.

Duck in orange sauce

1 duck (about 3lb/1.5kg)
5 oranges
1½oz/40g butter
sugar
1 cup/8fl oz/225ml stock
2 tablespoons Curaçao liqueur
salt and pepper

Melt butter in a heavy pan, season duck and brown lightly all over. Add stock and finely-chopped rind of two of the oranges. Cover pan and simmer until duck is cooked (about 60 minutes). Peel remaining oranges and chop peel thinly, cooking it in a little water until soft (about 3 minutes). Slice four of the peeled oranges into rounds and remove pips. Remove duck from pan and keep warm. Skim off excess fat from cooking juices, add the cooked orange peel, the juice of the fifth orange, a pinch of sugar and the Curaçao. Pour sauce over duck and garnish with orange rounds.

Chicken with honey and orange

4 chicken breasts
2 oranges
2 teaspoons runny honey
1 egg yolk
½ teaspoon basil
knob of butter
freshly-ground white pepper
salt

Melt butter in a frying pan, and cook chicken breasts until golden-brown (about 5 minutes each side). Peel and squeeze oranges. Lower heat once chicken is browned and push meat to side of pan. Add sliced orange peel and orange juice, then basil, salt and pepper and honey. Cover pan and simmer meat and sauce, still more or less separate, for 20-30 minutes. Turn meat half-way through cooking. Put chicken on a dish and keep warm.

Turn up heat and boil juices to reduce. Season to taste, adding a little more honey if desired. Thicken with egg yolk and pour over chicken. Garnish with slices of orange.

Orange Turkish delight

2 oranges
3 cups/24oz/750g sugar
3 tablespoons/3oz/90g
    cornflour
1 tablespoon/1oz/30g gelatine
⅔ cup/5fl oz/150ml water
orange food colouring
icing sugar

Soak gelatine in a little cold water. Grate rind of oranges, squeeze out juice and put juice and rind in a pan. Add water and sugar, and bring slowly to the boil once sugar has dissolved. Stir a little water into the cornflour and add to the gelatine syrup. Add cornflour/gelatine mixture to juice/sugar mixture and cook until clear, stirring continuously. Add orange colouring. Pour into a rectangular mould, to a depth of 1 inch/2.5cm. Allow to cool and set. Cut into cubes and dredge with icing sugar mixed with grated orange peel.

Baked pawpaw

2 large pawpaws
2oz/50g bacon
1 onion
1 teaspoon curry powder
1 cup/8fl oz/250ml chicken
    stock
salt
10oz/275g cooked chicken
grated cheese
1¼ cups/½ pint/300ml white
    sauce

Peel pawpaw, remove seeds and dice flesh. Cook for 10 minutes in salted water. Fry bacon and cook sliced onions in bacon fat until transparent. Sprinkle bacon and onion with curry powder, add chicken stock and bring to boil. Stir in white sauce and season to taste. Arrange alternate layers of pawpaw and chopped chicken in a baking dish, topping each layer with a little sauce. Sprinkle grated cheese over top layer and bake in moderate oven until golden-brown (about 30 minutes). (Meats other than chicken are equally tasty with pawpaw, though as far as possible one should match lamb with lamb stock, beef with beef stock, and so on.)

Pawpaw au gratin

2 large unripe pawpaws
1 chopped onion
1 large tomato
1½oz/40g butter
basil
thyme
breadcrumbs
grated Parmesan cheese

Sauté onion in butter until brown. Mix with diced pawpaw and sprinkle with basil and thyme. Cook for 10 minutes. Put mixture into an ovenproof dish, sprinkle breadcrumbs and Parmesan cheese on top and bake in a hot oven until the topping is golden and crunchy (about 10 minutes).

Baked pawpaw dessert

2 under-ripe pawpaws
cinnamon
sugar

Peel and slice pawpaws, removing seeds. Put a little water in the bottom of a buttered ovenproof dish, add pawpaw slices, sprinkle with sugar and cinammon, and bake in a moderate oven (325°F/160°C) for about 35 minutes.

Fluffy passionfruit dessert

8 passionfruits
5 tablespoons/5oz/150g sugar
juice of ½ lemon
3 egg whites

Halve passionfruits, scoop out the pulp and seeds, and purée in blender. Add sugar and lemon juice. Whip egg whites stiffly and fold into purée. Decorate with petits fours or maraschino cherries.

Passionfruit flambé with mango

4 passionfruits
1 ripe mango
knob of butter
2 tablespoons sugar
2 tablespoons Cointreau liqueur
2 tablespoons brandy

Halve passionfruits and scoop out pulp and seeds. Halve mango, and slice fruit away from the stone. Mix fruit with butter and sugar. Add brandy and Cointreau and flambé.

Passionfruit tartlets

4 passionfruits
4 small tart cases
3 tablespoons castor sugar
2 tablespoons thick cream
2 egg whites
lemon juice

Halve passionfruits, scoop out pulp and seeds. Mix pulp with sugar and cream and fill tart cases. Beat egg whites until stiff, adding a little castor sugar and a few drops of lemon juice. Spoon into filled tart cases and cook in a hot oven until the egg white turns golden.

Chinese fish with pineapple

10 Chinese dried mushrooms
1 cup/8fl oz/250ml water
1½lb/750g white fish fillets
juice of one lemon
3 tablespoons/3oz/75g flour
¼ cup/3 tablespoons/75ml oil
small fresh pineapple
⅓ cup/3 tablespoons/75ml mayonnaise
½ cup/4fl oz/125ml pineapple juice
curry powder
salt and pepper

Soak mushrooms in warm water for 15 minutes. Cut fish in pieces and sprinkle with lemon juice; leave to absorb, then sprinkle with salt. Flour fish and sauté in oil until golden-brown. Drain and keep warm. Dice pineapple; put trimmings (peel and core) in juicer or press out juice; put juice on one side.

Drain mushrooms, pressing out any surplus liquid. Gently sauté mushrooms and diced pineapple in fish pan for 10 minutes.

Blend mayonnaise and pineapple juice; warm gently in a small pan. Add curry powder, salt and pepper to taste. Spoon pineapple and mushroom over fish, then pour sauce over the top. Serve with boiled rice.

Pineapple sauerkraut

2 cups/1lb/500g sauerkraut
½ cup/4fl oz/125ml white wine
1 cup/7oz/200g fresh chopped pineapple
1 onion, finely chopped
1 teaspoon salt
1 teaspoon Kümmel liqueur (or dry sherry)
¼ teaspoon white pepper

Sauté onion in oil until transparent. Toss sauerkraut well, add wine, and cook in remaining oil, with the onion, for 20 minutes. Season with salt, pepper and Kümmel liqueur to taste, and finally stir in the chopped pineapple. An excellent accompaniment to pork or poultry.

Pineapple chicken

1 chicken
1 fresh pineapple
4 tablespoons/75ml Calvados
  (or brandy)
½ cup/4fl oz/100ml cream
butter
salt and pepper
2 sheets aluminium foil

Joint the chicken. Melt butter in a frying pan and sauté chicken pieces until golden brown all over. Cut pineapple into thick slices and remove skin. Lay aluminium sheets one on top of the other at right angles, and butter the top sheet generously. Put pineapple slices on the buttered sheet and season with salt and pepper.

  Season chicken pieces and put on top of pineapple slices adding a knob of butter, cream and Calvados. Fold foil carefully over chicken and seal tightly. Put the parcel into a preheated oven and cook for about an hour in a moderate oven.

Pomegranate ice

4 scoops lemon sorbet
1 pomegranate
redcurrant purée
1 cup double cream
chocolate flakes

Take four glasses, put a scoop of sorbet in each and top with a teaspoonful of pomegranate seeds and a dash of redcurrant purée. Finish each glass with whipped cream and chocolate flakes.

Quince pickle

1½lb/750g quinces
3 cups/25fl oz/750ml vinegar
2 cups/1lb/500g sugar
stick cinnamon
6 cloves

Peel and quarter quinces, put in covered pan with vinegar, cinnamon and cloves, and cook until almost soft (about 2 hours). Add a little water if needed. Add sugar and cook for another 30 minutes. Remove fruit and simmer liquid until syrupy. Replace fruit and leave to cool. Check next day that syrup has not thinned (this can happen if too much liquid seeps out of the fruit); if it has, re-simmer, leaving fruit in. Store in tightly-sealed pots. Keeps for a long time.

Rambutan jam

1lb/500g rambutans
1½ cups/12oz/350g sugar
2 cloves

Peel fruits, but do not remove pits. Cover with water, add cloves, bring to boil and cook until flesh comes away from the pits. Allow to cool. Remove pits and membranes. Cook pits in a little water until soft and add to fruit. Add sugar and simmer all ingredients for a further 20 minutes. Remove cloves before pouring into sterilized jars and sealing well. (This recipe can also be used to make lychee jam.)

Calves' liver with Sharon fruit

4 slices liver (4oz/120g each)
6 Sharon fruits
4 rashers slightly salted bacon
1 tablespoon clear honey
dash of thick cream
½ cup/4oz/100g ground
  hazelnuts
2oz/60g butter
pepper and salt
dash white wine

Season liver slices with salt and pepper and spread with honey. Melt butter in frying pan and lightly sauté. Remove from pan, wrap each slice in a rasher of bacon and return to pan. Cover pan and cook for 10 minutes.

  Meanwhile slice off tops of Sharon fruits and scoop out flesh. Purée flesh and stir in white wine and cream. Fill Sharon fruit shells with purée and sprinkle with ground hazelnuts. Place liver on a hot dish surrounded by fruit shells. Serve remaining purée separately. Accompany with a fresh green salad.

Stuffed Sharon fruit

4 Sharon fruits
1-2 bananas

2 slices pineapple
aniseed liqueur

Slice tops off Sharon fruits, scoop out flesh and sieve it. Mix with sliced bananas and pineapple chunks. Sprinkle with a few drops of aniseed liqueur. Fill fruit shells with mixture and replace 'lids'. Chill and serve.

Sharon fruit with medallions of pork

9oz/250g pork fillet
5 Sharon fruits
1 cup/8fl oz/225ml fresh
　cream

¼ cup/2fl oz/60ml gravy
4oz/100g butter
paprika
pepper and salt

If possible, choose one very ripe and four less ripe Sharon fruits. Cut off the tops of all of them, place on a sheet of buttered baking foil, and bake in an oven preheated to 400°F/200°C. Pour a drop of Calvados into them from time to time!

Cut pork fillet crosswise to make a dozen or so 'medallions', flatten them and season with salt, paprika and freshly-ground pepper. Melt butter in pan and sauté medallions on both sides. Add Calvados and quickly flambé. Remove medallions from pan and keep warm.

Take ripest Sharon fruit out of oven, scoop out pulp and mash with a fork. Add to meat together with fresh cream and a knob of butter. Arrange the baked fruit around the medallions in their sauce. Very good served with jacket potatoes or potato croquettes.

Stewed tamarillos

8 tamarillos
2 tablespoons sugar

1 cup water

Boil water and pour over tamarillos. Leave to stand for 3 minutes. Skin the fruits and cut in half lengthways. Lay flat side down in an ovenproof dish and sprinkle with sugar. Cover and bake for 10-15 minutes in a hot oven. Good served with roast meat.

Tamarillo sorbet

10 tamarillos
6 tablespoons/6oz/160g sugar
1 clove
1 strip orange peel
1 cup/9fl oz/250ml water
½ cup/5fl oz/125ml thick cream
wafer biscuits
juice of lime
juice of orange

Peel tamarillos (pop them in boiling water for 3 minutes to make skins easy to remove). Purée flesh using a sieve or blender. Add juice from the orange and lime.

Boil sugar, clove and orange peel, then sieve and cool. Mix syrup with tamarillo purée and freeze it, stirring occasionally to keep it frothy. Scoop mixture into glasses and decorate with wafer biscuits and whipped cream.

Créole watermelon cocktail

½ small watermelon
½ cup/4fl oz/100ml thick cream
1 teaspoon curry powder
4 tablespoons mayonnaise
2 tablespoons tomato ketchup
2 tablespoons sherry
4oz/100g peeled shrimps
parsley
salt

Halve watermelon, remove seeds and chop flesh. Mix all but a few pieces of watermelon with shrimps. Whip cream until stiff, then stir in sherry and curry powder, mayonnaise, tomato ketchup and a little salt. Divide melon and prawn mixture between four cocktail glasses and top with sauce. Garnish with a sprig of parsley and reserved pieces of melon. Serve chilled, preferably with hot buttered toast!

Chicken and watermelon salad

1 watermelon
8oz/225g cooked chicken meat
1 green pepper
1 cucumber
fresh lettuce
mustard
oil and vinegar
salt and pepper

Halve watermelon, remove seeds and chop flesh. Add diced chicken. Make a dressing with oil, vinegar, salt, pepper and mustard and pour over melon. Cover, and chill for 1 hour in the refrigerator. Served on a bed of fresh lettuce leaves, garnished with strips of pepper and cucumber.

Watermelon with wine

1 watermelon
4 cloves
red or white wine

Halve watermelon, remove seeds and chop flesh. Put melon in a dish, add cloves (or a pinch of ground cloves), and sufficient wine to cover. Leave to stand for at least 30 minutes so that flavours blend. Serve ice-cold.

General index

Index of botanical names

Acknowledgements

All the photographs in this book are by Kees Jansen, with the exception of: front and cover, pages 1, 2/3, 4, 9 and 161-175 Chris Steffens Fotografie, Amsterdam; pages 6, 12, 26, 48, 62, 72 and 150 Fotobureau Koninklijk Instituut voor de Tropen; pages 7, 8 (bottom right, middle right, upper right) and 107 Ing. Chr. Vos; page 118 (top) J. E. Reinhoudt; page 8 (left) Proefstation Wilhelminadorp.

This book is the result of the enthusiastic cooperation of many people, companies and institutions. For supplying information, fruit samples, recipes and additional photographs, the publishers would like to thank Agrexco Agricultural Export Co. Limited, Schiedam; Bangkok Trading and Export, Bangkok; Bedrijfschap voor de Groothandel en de Tussenpersonen in Groenten en Fruit, The Hague; Carmel Promotiekantoor voor de Benelux, Schmiedam; COLEACP, Paris (Rungis); C. H. Heezen (Hector BV Int., Rotterdam); Interfresh BV, Amsterdam; Internationale Fruchtimport Gesellschaft Weichert & Co, Hamburg/Rotterdam; Koninklijk Instituut voor de Tropen, Amsterdam; New Zealand Kiwi Fruit Authority, Amsterdam; Produktschap voor Groenten en Fruit, The Hague; Proefstation voor de Fruitteelt, Wilhelminadorp; Saopaulexotic, Sao Paolo; Spania, Alkmaar; Gebr. Spiering BV, Amsterdam; Stichting Propaganda Groenten en Fruit, The Hague; The Outspan Organization, Barendrecht; The Summer Orange Office, London; Jan Visser (Westland Import Int., Poeldijk); Jens van der Vorm; Windig BV, Amsterdam; Wim Wagemaker (ISPC, Breda).